THE C. F. MONROE CO.

MANUFACTURERS OF

WAVE CREST GEMS
WEDDING & HOLIDAY NOVELTIES.

OFFICE AND FACTORY,
MERIDEN, CONN.

NEW YORK SALESROOM,
28 BARCLAY ST.

Foreword

When I first started collecting Wave Crest and other glass of the C.F. Monroe Co. in 1971, there was essentially no published information on the company. I obtained virtually all of my information from writing questions to R. Shawn Bradway in New England, and receiving 3-5 page letters from him in return.

Then, in the late 1970s, Elsa Grimmer published her book, and the company's catalog from 1900-1901. In 1987, my book Wave Crest, The Glass of C.F. Monroe was published, along with reproductions of the 1895-1896 catalog, and the supplement to the 1900-1901 catalog.

Various advertisements began to appear, especially from the jeweler's magazine Keystone, adding to our knowledge of the company. Recently, Carrol Lyle and Whitney Newland, major collectors and contributors to my book, obtained and published the 1906-07 catalog, replete with extensive sections on cut glass, metal products, and our first catalog pictures of "Nakara." We have yet to obtain anything similar on "Kelva."

With this catalog, 1902-1903, we have our first look at what everyone has heretofore referred to as "wall plaques." We can now see that the company called them "Gems".

Rumor has it, that when the company went out of business in 1916, everything was thrown away. There was certainly no reason to save catalogs and records for future collectors a century later. We now have one more piece of the puzzle.

I hope you enjoy it.

Sincerely,

Wilfred R. Cohen
September, 1999

AP
Antique Publications
A Division of The Glass Press, Inc.

ISBN 1-57080-071-5

The Glass Press, Inc.
P.O. Box 553 • Marietta, Ohio 45750-0553

THE C. F. MONROE CO.

MANUFACTURERS OF

RICH CUT GLASS

OFFICE AND FACTORY,
MERIDEN, CONN.

NEW YORK SALESROOM,
28 BARCLAY ST.

FACTORIES OF THE C. F. MONROE CO., MERIDEN, CONN.

EXTERIOR VIEW NEW YORK STORE, 28 BARCLAY STREET.

INTERIOR VIEW OF OUR NEW YORK STORE, 28 BARCLAY STREET.

FACTORY OFFICES, MERIDEN, CONN.

FACTORY OFFICES, MERIDEN, CONN.

INDEX TO ILLUSTRATIONS

14-Inch Footed Punch Bowl

SYLPH

List each $84.00

14-Inch Footed Punch Bowl

SUNBURST

List each $170.00

14-Inch Footed Punch Bowl

NORMA

List each $66 00

Starlight Pattern, Patented May 13, 1902.

	SUNBURST	SYLPH	STARLIGHT	SATELLITE	NORMA	COMET
12-Inch Punch Bowl . . . . each	. . . .	$48.00	. . . .	. . . .	$32.00	. . . .
14-Inch Punch Bowl . . . . each	. . . .	. . . .	. . . .	. . . .	48.00	. . . .
No. 520 Lemonade . . . . dozen	. . . .	27.00	. . . .	. . . .	22.00	$18.00
No. 730 Lemonade . . . . dozen	. . . .	27.00	$32.00	$22.00	24.00	. . . .

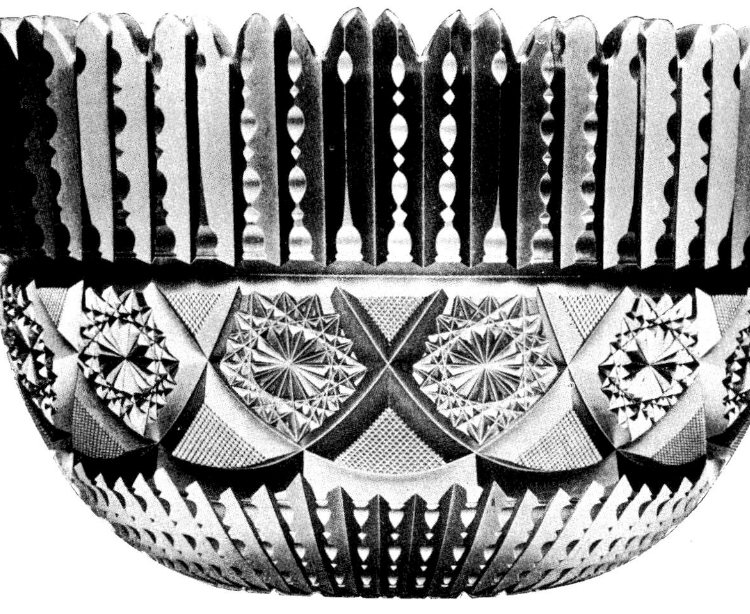

12-Inch Deep Bowl
SYLPH

No. 730 Lemonade
NORMA

No. 520 Lemonade
SYLPH

14-Inch Round Bowl
NORMA

Starlight Pattern, Patented May 13, 1902.

	SUNBURST	ALPHA	OLGA	ALLITA	NARADA	STARLIGHT	SYLPH	SATELLITE	NORMA	COMET
No. 125 Round Bowl, 7 Inches . . . each	. . . .	. . .	. . . .	$10.00	$7.50	. . . .	$8.50	$8.00	$7.00	$6.00
No. 125 Round Bowl, 8 Inches . . . each	$20.00	$20.00	$13.50	12.00	12 50	$11.00	11.00	9.00	8.00	6.50
No. 125 Round Bowl, 9 Inches . . . each	25.00	24.00	18.00	17.00	15.50	15.00	12.50	10.00	10.00	9.00
No. 125 Round Bowl, 10 Inches . . . each	32.00	31.00	22.00	21.00	20.50	19.00	17.50	. . . .	. . . .	. . . .
No. 700 Flat Bowl, 7 Inches . . . . each	. . . .	. . . .	. . .	10.00	7 50	. . . .	8.50	8.00	7.00	6.00
No. 700 Flat Bowl, 8 Inches . . . . each	20.00	20.00	13.50	12 00	12.50	11.00	11.00	9.00	8.00	6.50
No. 700 Flat Bowl, 9 Inches . . . . each	25.00	24.00	18.00	17.00	15.50	15.00	12.50	10.00	10.00	9.00
No. 700 Flat Bowl, 10 Inches . . . . each	32.00	31.00	22.00	21.00	20.50	19.00	17.50	. . . .	. . . .	. . . .

No. 125 9-Inch Bowl
SUNBURST

No. 125 9-Inch Bowl
ALPHA

No. 125 9-Inch Bowl
STARLIGHT

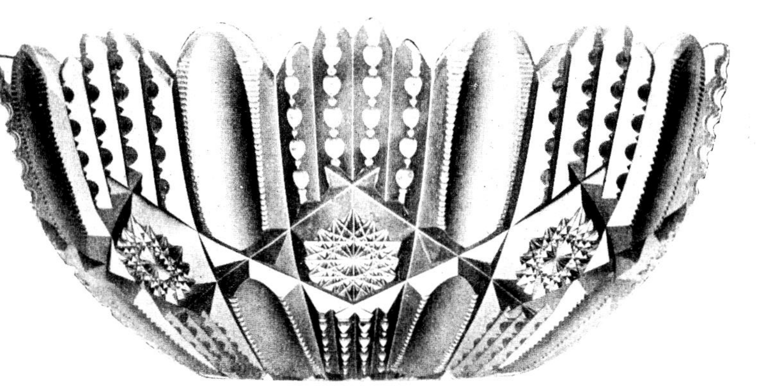

No. 125 9-Inch Bowl
NARADA

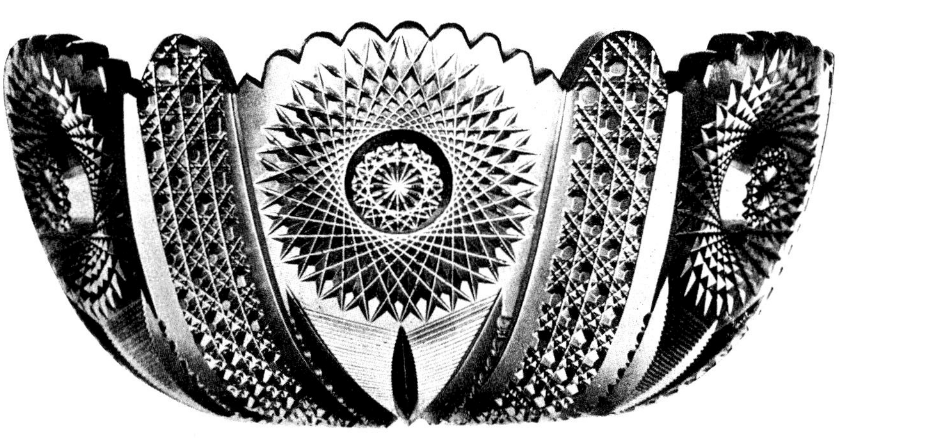

No. 125 10-Inch Bowl
OLGA

No. 700 9-Inch Bowl
ALLITA

Starlight Pattern, Patented May 13, 1902.

	ALPHA	OLGA	SYLPH	ALLITA	STARLIGHT	PRISM
No. 1625 Bowl, 8 Inches . . . . . each	$23.00	. . . .	. . . .	. . . .	. . .	. . . .
No. 1625 Bowl, 9 Inches . . . . . each	24.00	. . . .	. . . .	. . . .	. . . .	. . . .
No. 1625 Bowl, 10 Inches . . . . . each	32.00	. . . .	. . . .	$27.00	. . . .	. . . .
No. 300 Bowl, 8x11 Inches . . . . . each	. . . .	. . . .	. . . .	. . . .	$16.00	. . . .
Bell Shape Bowl, 8 Inches . . . . . each	. . . .	. . . .	$13 00	. . . .	. . . .	. . . .
Bell Shape Bowl, 9 Inches . . . . . each	. . . .	. . . .	18 00	. . . .	. . . .	$14.00
No. 1006 Bowl, 9 Inches . . . . . each	. . . .	$19.00	. . .	19.00	. . . .	. . . .

No. 300 Oval Nut Bowl
STARLIGHT

No. 1625 9-Inch Bowl
ALPHA

No. 1006 9-Inch Bowl
ALLITA

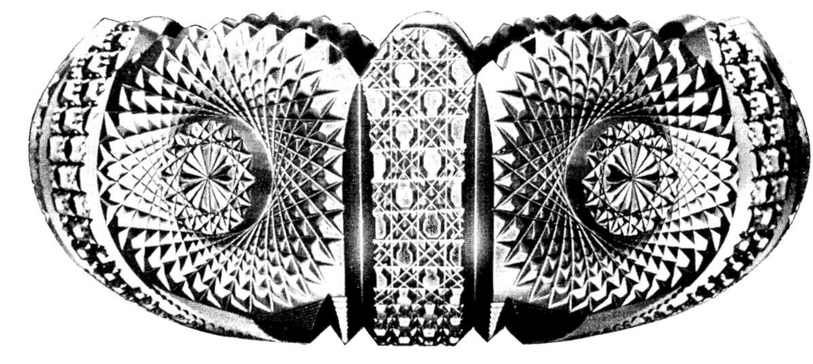

No. 1006 9-Inch Bowl
OLGA

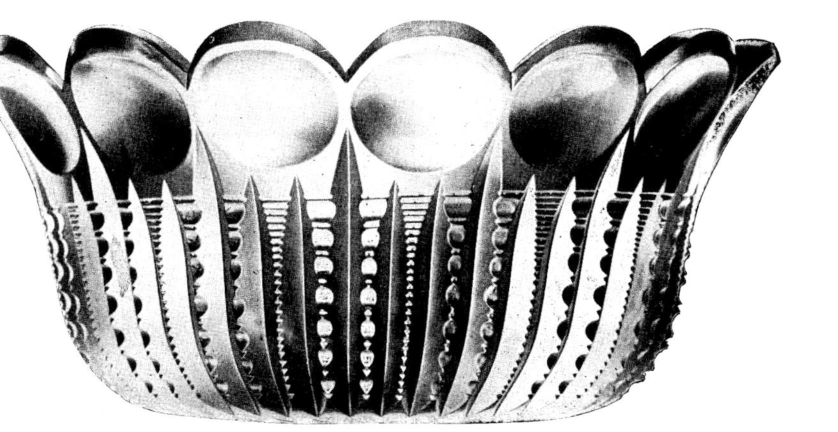

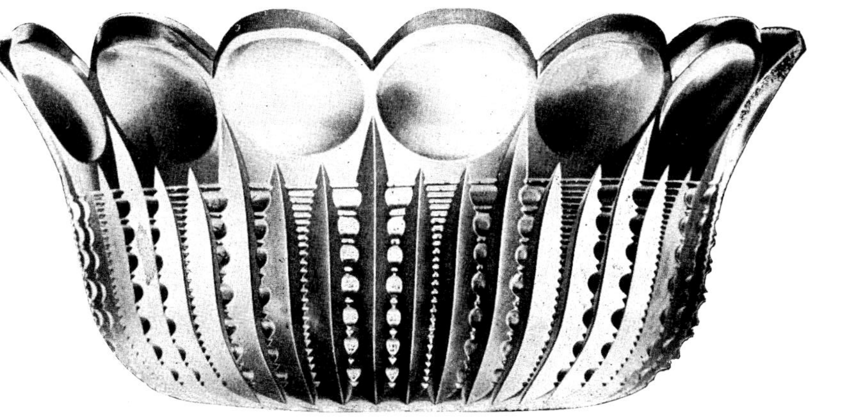

9-Inch Bell Shape Bowl
PRISM

9-Inch Bell Shape Bowl
SYLPH

Starlight Pattern, Patented May 13, 1902.

	SUNBURST	ALPHA	OLGA	ALLITA	SYLPH	NARADA	STARLIGHT	SATELLITE	NORMA	COMET
No. 256 Bowl, 7-Inch . . each	. . . .	. . . .	. . . .	. . . .	. . . .	. . . .	$12.00	. . . .	. . . .	. . . .
No. 256 Bowl, 8-Inch . . each	. . . .	. . . .	. . . .	. . . .	. . .	. . . .	14.00	. . . .	. . . .	. . . .
No. 256 Bowl, 9-Inch . . each	. . . .	. . . .	. . . .	. . . .	. . . .	. . . .	20.00	. . . .	. . . .	. . . .
No. 125 Bowl, 7-Inch . . each	. . . .	. . . .	. . . .	$10.00	$8.50	$7.50	. . . .	$8.00	$7 00	$6.00
No. 125 Bowl, 8-Inch . . each	$20.00	$20.00	$13 50	12 00	11.00	12.50	11.00	9.00	8.00	6.50
No. 125 Bowl, 9-Inch . . each	25.00	24.00	18.00	17.00	12.50	15.50	15.00	10.00	10.00	9.00
No. 125 Bowl, 10-Inch . . each	32.c0	31 00	22.00	21 00	17.50	20.50	19.00	. . . .	. . . .	. . . .

No. 256 Square Shape Bowl
STARLIGHT

No. 125 8-Inch Bowl
SATELLITE

No. 125 9-Inch Bowl
SYLPH

No. 125 8-Inch Bowl
NORMA

No. 125 8-Inch Bowl
COMET

Starlight Pattern, Patented May 13, 1902.

	OLGA	ALLITA	SYLPH	STARLIGHT	SATELLITE	COMET
No. 1040 Ice Cream Tray . . . . each	$40.00	. . . .	$30.00	. . . .	. . . .	. . . .
7-Inch Ice Cream Plate . . . . each	9.00	$9.00	7.00	$7.00	$6.00	. . . .
8-Inch Comport . . . . each	. . . .	. . . .	. . . .	. . . .	. . . .	$11.00

8-Inch Comport
COMET

No. 1040 Ice Cream Tray
OLGA

7-Inch Ice Cream Plate
SYLPH

No. 1040 Ice Cream Tray
SYLPH

	ALLITA	SATELLITE	COMET	SYLPH
5-Inch Butter Plate . . . . each	. . . .	. . . .	$7.50	. . . .
5-Inch Butter Cover . . . . each	. . . .	. . . .	8.00	. . . .
6-Inch Cheese Plate . . . . each	$11.00	. . . .	. . . .	. . . .
6-Inch Cheese Cover . . . . each	15.00	. . . .	. . . .	. . . .
3-Inch Butter . . . . dozen	24.00	$16.00	. . . .	$18.00

3-Inch Butter
SYLPH

3-Inch Butter
SATELLITE

5-Inch Butter Dish and Cover
COMET

6-Inch Cheese Dish and Cover
ALLITA

Starlight Pattern, Patented May 13, 1902.

	SUNBURST	ALLITA	OLGA	SYLPH	STARLIGHT	NARADA	SATELLITE	NORMA	COMET
5-Inch Round Nappy . . . each	. . . .	. . . .	. . . .	$4.00	$4 00	$3.00	$2.70	$2.50	$2.25
6-Inch Round Nappy . . . each	. . . .	$5.50	$5.50	5.00	4.50	3.50	3.00	3.00	2.67
7-Inch Round Nappy . . . each	. . . .	10.00	10.00	6.50	7.00	7.00	5.50	5.50	4.50
8 Inch Round Nappy . . . each	. . . .	12.00	12.50	9.00	9 00	8.00	6.00	6.50	6.00
9-Inch Round Nappy . . . each	$18.00	13 50	14.00	10.00	12.00	10.50	. . . .	. . . .	. . . .
10-Inch Round Nappy . . . each	. . . .	. . . .	18.50	. . . .	. . .	. . .	. . . .	. . . .	. . . .

5-Inch Round Nappy
STARLIGHT

9-Inch Round Nappy
SUNBURST

6-Inch Round Nappy
OLGA

6-Inch Round Nappy
ALLITA

6-Inch Round Nappy
SYLPH

Starlight Pattern, Patented May 13, 1902.

	SUNBURST	OLGA	ALLITA	SYLPH	STARLIGHT	NARADA	SATELLITE	NORMA	COMET
5-Inch Handled Nappy . . each	....	....	....	....	$4.50	$3.50	$3.00	$3.00	$2.50
6-Inch Handled Nappy . . each	....	....	....	$5.50	5.00	4.00	3.50	3.50	3.00
5-Inch Round Nappy . . . each	....	....	....	4.00	4.00	3.00	2.70	2.50	2.25
6-Inch Round Nappy . . . each	....	$5.50	$5.50	5.00	4.50	3.50	3.00	3.00	2.67
7-Inch Round Nappy . . . each	....	....	....	6.50	7.00	7.00	5.50	5 50	4.50
8-Inch Round Nappy . . . each	....	12.50	12.00	9.00	9.00	8.00	6.00	6 50	6.00
9-Inch Round Nappy . . . each	$18.00	14.00	13.50	10.00	12.00	10.50	....	....	....
10-Inch Round Nappy . . . each	....	18.50	....	....	....	....	....	....	....

6-Inch Handled Nappy
STARLIGHT

6-Inch Round Nappy
NARADA

6-Inch Round Nappy
SATELLITE

5-Inch Round Nappy
COMET

6-Inch Round Nappy
NORMA

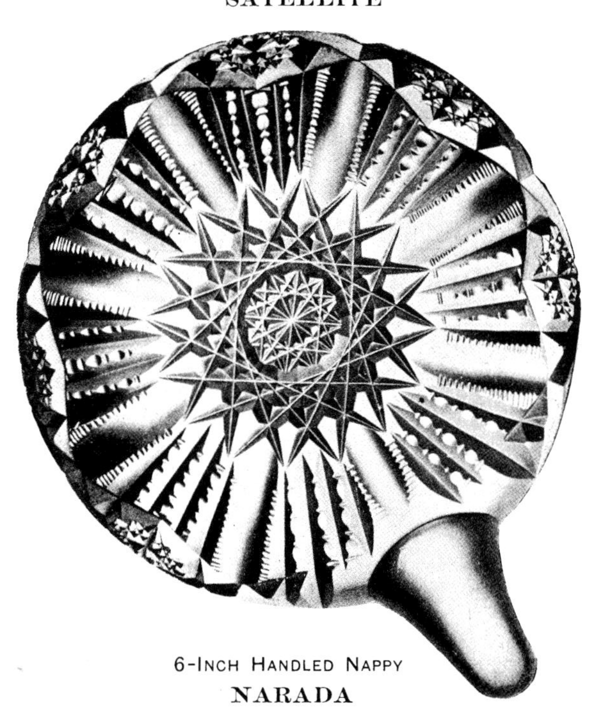

6-Inch Handled Nappy
NARADA

Starlight Pattern, Patented May 13, 1902.

	SUNBURST	OLGA	ALLITA	SYLPH	STARLIGHT	NARADA	SATELLITE	NORMA	COMET
No. 6395 Bon Bon . . . . each	$12.50	. . . .	. . . .	. . . .	$6.50	. . . .	$5.50	$6.00	. . . .
5-Inch Star Nappy . . . . each	. . . .	. . . .	. . . .	$4 00	. . . .	. . . .	. . . .	. . . .	. . . .
6-Inch Star Nappy . . . . each	. . . .	. . . .	. . . .	5 00	. . . .	. . . .	. . . .	. . . .	. . . .
7-Inch Star Nappy . . . . each	. . . .	. . . .	. . . .	6.50	. . . .	. . . .	. . . .	. . . .	. . . .
8-Inch Star Nappy . . . . each	. . . .	. . . .	. . . .	9.50	. . . .	. . . .	. . . .	. . . .	. . . .
No. 1050 Tray . . . . . . each	. . . .	$8.00	. . . .	. . . .	. . . .	$6.00	5.50	. . . .	. . . .
No. 350 Bon Bon . . . . each	. . . .	. . . .	$8.50	. . . .	. . . .	. . . .	. . . .	. . . .	$5.00
No 37 Olive or Spoon Tray each	. . . .	. . . .	. . . .	. . . .	. . . .	. . . .	3.50	3.00	3.00

No. 6395 Bon Bon
SATELLITE (Side View)

No. 1050 Tray
OLGA

No. 350 Bon Bon
ALLITA

No. 6395 Bon Bon
SUNBURST (Flat View)

No. 350 Bon Bon
COMET

No. 37 Olive or Spoon Tray
SATELLITE

7-Inch Star Nappy
SYLPH

	OLGA	NARADA	SATELLITE	NORMA	COMET
No. 496 Bon Bon . . . . each	. . . .	. . . .	. . . .	. . .	$3.50
No. 596 Bon Bon . . . . each	. . . .	. . . .	. . . .	$4.00	. . . .
No. 796 Bon Bon . . . . each	. . . .	. . .	. . . .	. . . .	3.00
No. 305 Bon Bon . . . . each	. . . .	. . . .	. . . .	3.00	. . . .
No. 1050 Tray . . . . each	$8.00	$6.00	$5.50	. . . .	. . . .
No. 141 Olive . . . . each	. . . .	. . . .	4.50	. . . .	4.00
No. 512 Bon Bon . . . . each	. . . .	. . . .	3.00	. . . .	. . . .

No. 596 Bon Bon
NORMA

No. 496 Bon Bon
COMET

No. 796 Bon Bon
COMET

No. 305 Olive
NORMA

No. 141 Olive (Flat View)
COMET

No. 1050 Tray
SATELLITE

No. 512 Bon Bon
SATELLITE

No. 141 Olive (Side View)
SATELLITE

Starlight Pattern, Patented May 13, 1902.

	ALLITA	SYLPH	STARLIGHT	NARADA	SATELLITE	NORMA	COMET
5-Inch Handled Nappy . . . . each	. . . .	. . . .	$4.50	$3.50	$3.00	$3.00	$2.50
7-Inch Plate . . . . each	$9.00	$7.00	7.00	. . . .	6 00	. . . .	. . . .

5-Inch Handled Nappy
NORMA

5-Inch Handled Nappy
SATELLITE

7-Inch Plate
ALLITA

7-Inch Plate
SYLPH

7-Inch Plate
SATELLITE

Starlight Pattern, Patented May 13, 1902.

	OLGA	SYLPH	STARLIGHT	NARADA	NORMA	SATELLITE	COMET
6 Inch Rolled Spoon . . . . each	. . . .	$5.50	$5.00	$4.00	. . . .	$3.50	$3.50
No. 217 Spoon . . . . each	. . . .	. . . .	. . . .	. . . .	. . . .	5.00	. . . .
No. 547 Spoon . . . . each	. . . .	. . . .	. . . .	. . . .	. . . .	4.00	. . . .
No. 1600 Celery . . . . each	$13.00	13.00	. . . .	. . . .	$8.00	8.00	. . . .
No. 1400 Celery . . . . each	. . .	. . . .	. . . .	. . . .	7.00	7.00	6.00

6-Inch Rolled Spoon
SATELLITE

6-Inch Rolled Spoon
NARADA

6-Inch Rolled Spoon
SYLPH

No. 547 Spoon
SATELLITE

No. 217 Spoon
SATELLITE

6-Inch Rolled Spoon
STARLIGHT

No. 1600 Celery
SATELLITE

No. 1400 Celery
COMET

Starlight Pattern, Patented May 13, 1902.

	SUNBURST	OLGA	SYLPH	NARADA	STARLIGHT	NORMA	COMET	SATELLITE
No. 1300 Celery Tray . . . . each	$17.00	. . . .	. . . .	$10.00	$10.50	. . . .	$8.50	. . . .
No. 1600 Celery Tray . . . . each	. . . .	$13.00	$13.00	. . . .	. . . .	$8.00	. . . .	$8.00

No. 1300 Celery
SUNBURST

No. 1600 Celery
SYLPH

No. 1600 Celery
OLGA

No. 1300 Celery
NARADA

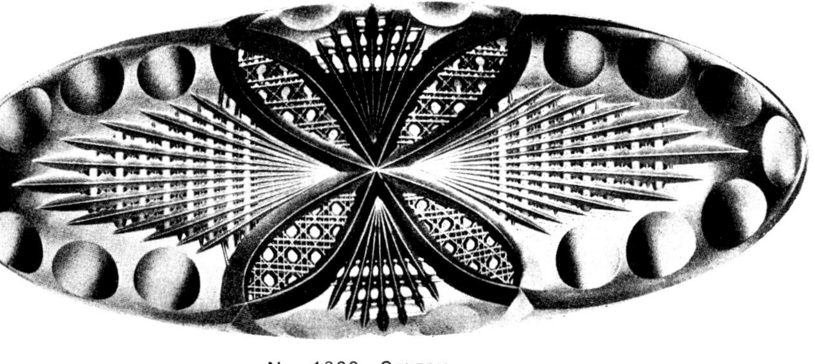

No. 1300 Celery
STARLIGHT

No. 1300 Celery
COMET

	ALPHA	OLGA	NARADA
No. 909 Vase, 12 Inches high . . . . each	$36.00	. . . .	. . .
No. 640 Vase, 12 Inches high . . . . each	. . . .	$36.00	. . . .
Cylinder Vase, 12 Inches high . . . . each	. . . .	. . . .	$18.00

No. 640 Vase, 12 Inches

OLGA

Cylinder Vase, 12 Inches

NARADA

No. 909 Vase, 12 Inches

ALPHA

Starlight Pattern, Patented May 13, 1902.

	SUNBURST	STARLIGHT	PRISM
No. 1045 Vase, 10½ Inches high . . . . . . each	. . . .	$20.00	$14.00
No. 910 Vase, 8 Inches high . . . . . . each	$36.00	. . . .	. . . .
No. 3708 Loving Cup, 3 Pints . . . . . . each	. . . .	. . . .	15.50

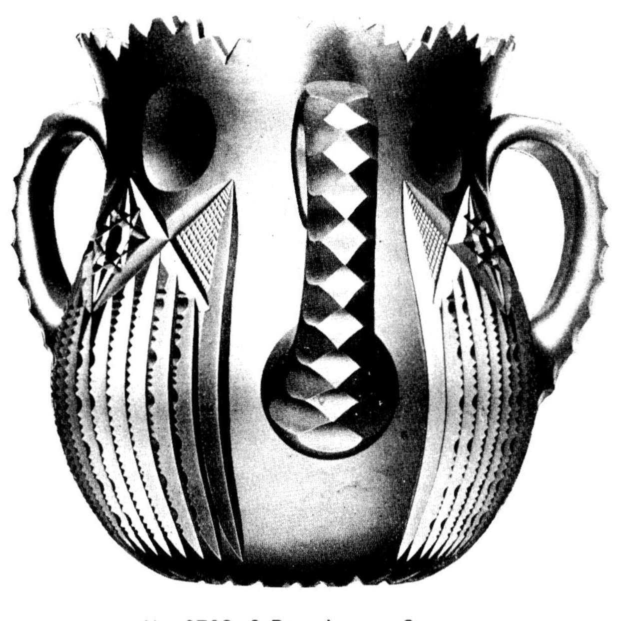

No. 3708 3-Pint Loving Cup

PRISM

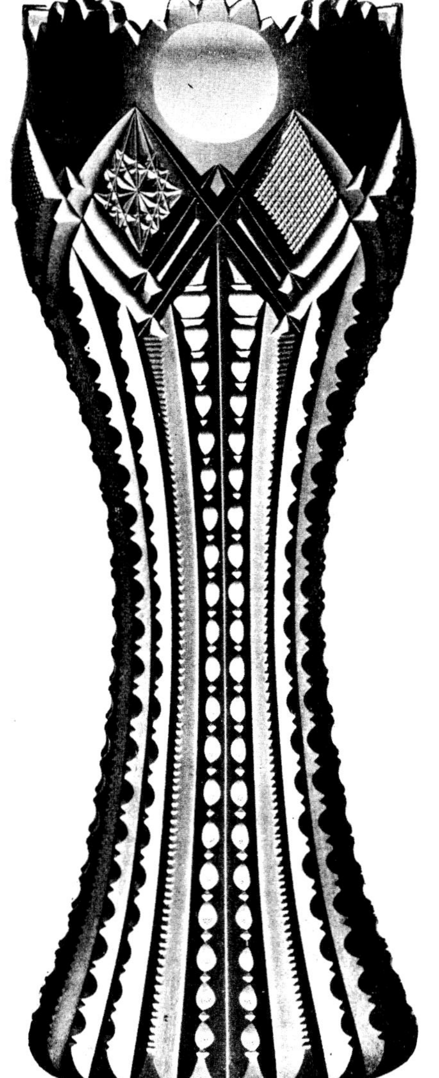

No. 1045 10½-Inch Vase

PRISM

No. 910 8-Inch Vase

SUNBURST

Starlight Pattern, Patented May 13, 1902.

	STARLIGHT	PRISM	SATELLITE	NORMA
Trumpet Vase, 8 Inches . . . . . each	$5.50	$5.00	$5.00	$4.50
Trumpet Vase, 10 Inches . . . . . each	7.50	7.00	7.00	6.50
Trumpet Vase, 12 Inches . . . . . each	10.50	10.50	9.00	8.00
Trumpet Vase, 14 Inches . . . . . each	14.00	. . . .	. . . .	. . . .
No. 767 Vase, 14 Inches . . . . . each	. . . .	14.00	. . .	. . . .

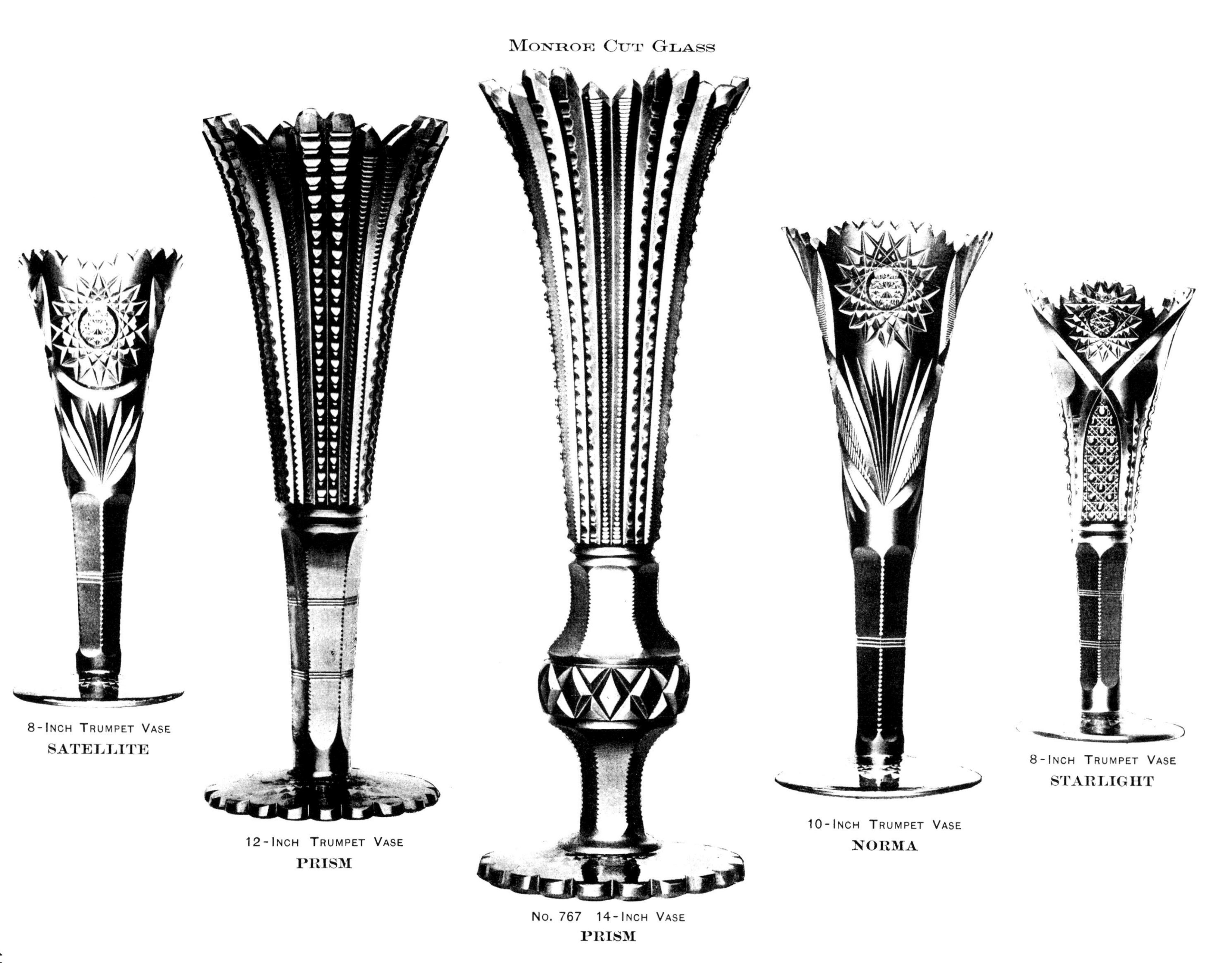

8-Inch Trumpet Vase
SATELLITE

12-Inch Trumpet Vase
PRISM

No. 767 14-Inch Vase
PRISM

10-Inch Trumpet Vase
NORMA

8-Inch Trumpet Vase
STARLIGHT

	No. 1	No. 2	No. 3	No. 4	No. 5	No. 6	No. 7	No. 8	No. 9	No. 10
Vases, Exclusive Shapes . . . . each	$6.00	$5.00	$3 50	$3.50	$6.50	$5.50	$5.50	$4.00	$6.50	$7.00

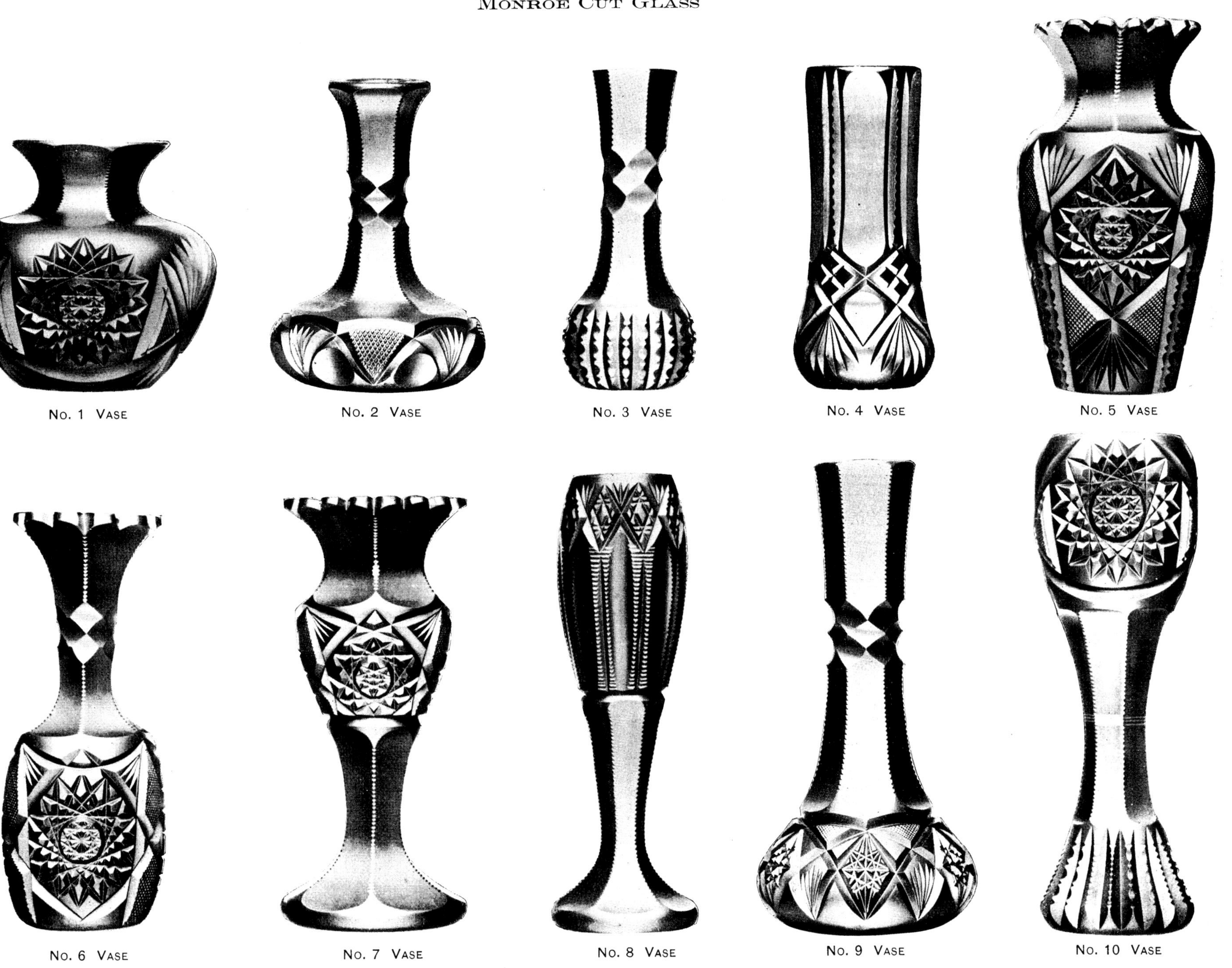

No. 1 Vase

No. 2 Vase

No. 3 Vase

No. 4 Vase

No. 5 Vase

No. 6 Vase

No. 7 Vase

No. 8 Vase

No. 9 Vase

No. 10 Vase

	ALPHA	SYLPH	NARADA	SATELLITE	COMET	PRISM
Globe Cologne, No. 1, 27 Oz. . . . . each	$18.00	$13.00	. . . .	$10.50	$9.50	. . . .
Globe Cologne, No. 2, 16 Oz. . . . . each	. . . .	10.00	. . . .	8.00	8.00	. . . .
Globe Cologne, No. 3, 7 Oz. . . . . each	. . . .	8.00	. . . .	7.00	7.00	. . . .
No. 682 Cologne, 6 Oz. . . . . each	. . . .	. . . .	$6.00	. . . .	. . . .	. . . .
No. 682 Cologne, 8 Oz. . . . . each	. . . .	. . . .	8.00	. . . .	. . . .	. . . .
No. 682 Cologne, 12 Oz. . . . . each	. . . .	. . . .	9.00	. . . .	. . . .	. . . .
Round Cologne, 6 Oz. . . . . each	. . . .	. . . .	. . . .	. . . .	. . . .	$6.00
Round Cologne, 8 Oz. . . . . each	. . . .	. . . .	. . . .	. . . .	. . . .	7.00
Round Cologne, 12 Oz. . . . . each	. . . .	. . . .	. . . .	. . . .	. . . .	8.00

No. 682 8-Oz. Cologne
NARADA

No. 2 16-Oz. Globe Cologne
SYLPH

No. 3 7-Oz. Globe Cologne
COMET

Round 12-Oz. Cologne
PRISM

No. 1 27-Oz. Globe Cologne
SATELLITE

No. 1 27-Oz. Globe Cologne
ALPHA

	NIAGARA	NARADA	SATELLITE	NORMA	COMET	SPECIAL
No. 2 Carafe, Niagara . . . . each	$7 00	. . . .	. . .	. . . .	. . . .	. . . .
Rose Globe, 5 Inches . . . . each	. . . .	$8.00	$7.00	$5.50	$5.00	. . . .
Rose Globe, 6 Inches . . . . each	. . . .	10.00	9.00	7.50	7.00	. . . .
Rose Globe, 7 Inches . . . . each	. . . .	13.00	11.00	9.50	9.00	. . . .
No. 539 Candlestick . . . . each	. . . .	. . . .	. . . .	. . . .	. . . .	$8 00

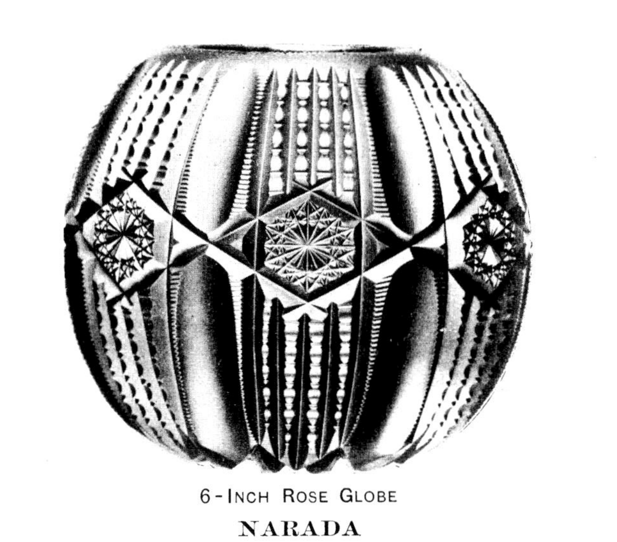

6-Inch Rose Globe
NARADA

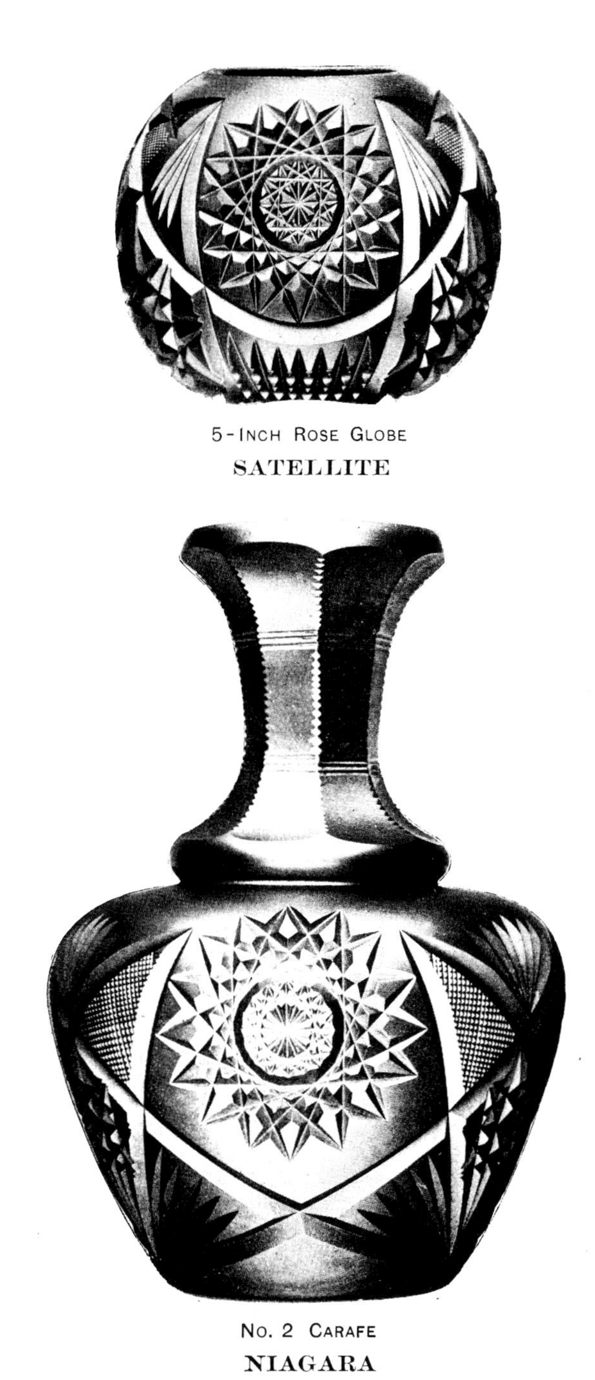

5-Inch Rose Globe
SATELLITE

No. 2 Carafe
NIAGARA

No. 539 Candlestick
SPECIAL

7-Inch Rose Globe
COMET

Starlight Pattern, Patented May 13, 1902.

	ALLITA	STARLIGHT	NARADA	SATELLITE	COMET	NORMA	SYLPH
Quart Round Carafe . . . . each	$10.50	$8 00	$7.50	$6.50	$5.00	$5.50	$10.00
Quart Squat Carafe . . . . each	10.50	8.00	7.50	6.50	5.00	5.50	10.00
No. 520 Tumblers . . . . dozen	. . . .	30.00	. . . .	26.50	24.00	. . . .	36.00
No. 730 Tumblers . . . . dozen	. . . .	30.00	. . . .	. . . .	. . . .	. . . .	. . . .
No. 176 Tumblers . . . . dozen	. . . .	. . . .	. . . .	20 00	19.00	. . . .	. . . .

No. 520 ½ Pint Tumbler
COMET

Quart Round Carafe
COMET

Quart Round Carafe
ALLITA

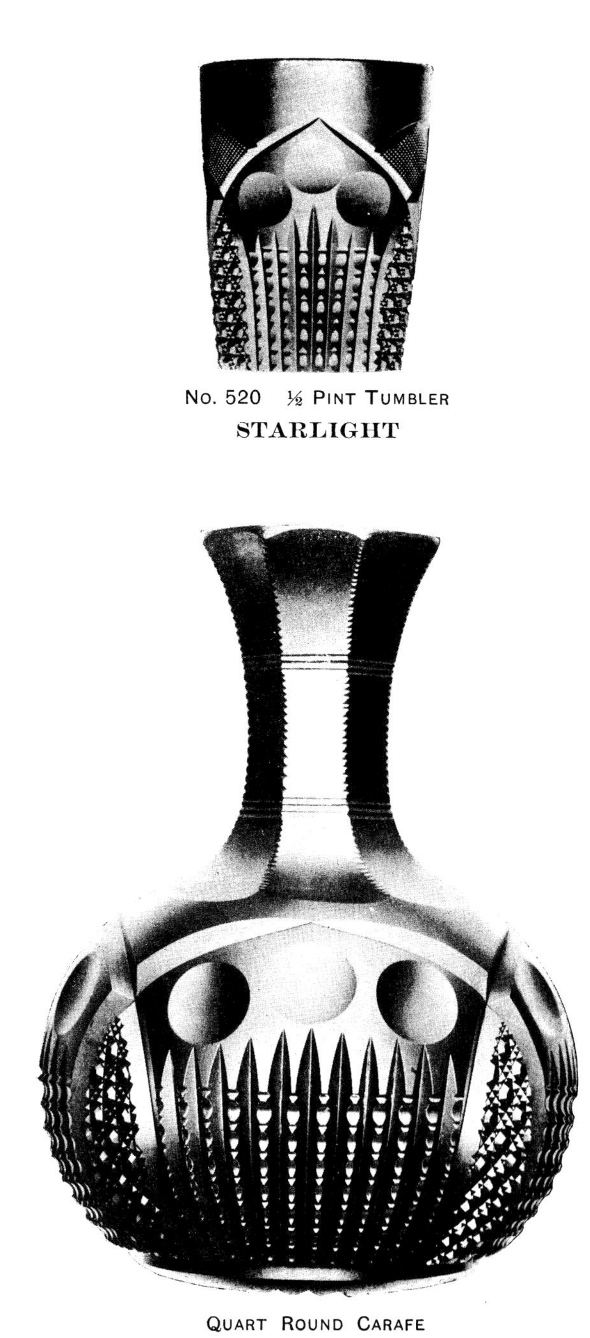

No. 520 ½ Pint Tumbler
STARLIGHT

Quart Round Carafe
STARLIGHT

Starlight Pattern, Patented May 13, 1902.

	ALLITA	STARLIGHT	NARADA	SATELLITE	NORMA	COMET	SYLPH
Quart Round Carafe . . . . each	$10.50	$8.00	$7.50	$6.50	$5 50	$5.00	$10 00
Quart Squat Carafe . . . . each	10.50	8.00	7.50	6.50	5.50	5.00	10.00

QUART SQUAT CARAFE
STARLIGHT

QUART SQUAT CARAFE
SATELLITE

QUART ROUND CARAFE
NARADA

Starlight Pattern, Patented May 13, 1902.

		ALLITA	SYLPH	STARLIGHT	NARADA
No. 698	Ice Tub . . . . each	$13.00	. . . .	$10.50	. . . .
	Two-Handled Straight Ice Tub . . . . . . each	. . . .	. . . .	. . . .	$12.00
No. 141	Ice Tub . . . . each	. . . .	$14.00	. . . .	. . . .

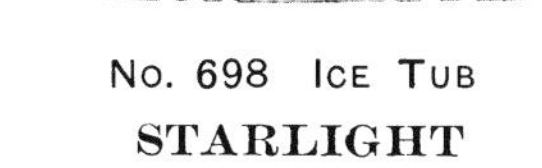

No. 698 Ice Tub
STARLIGHT

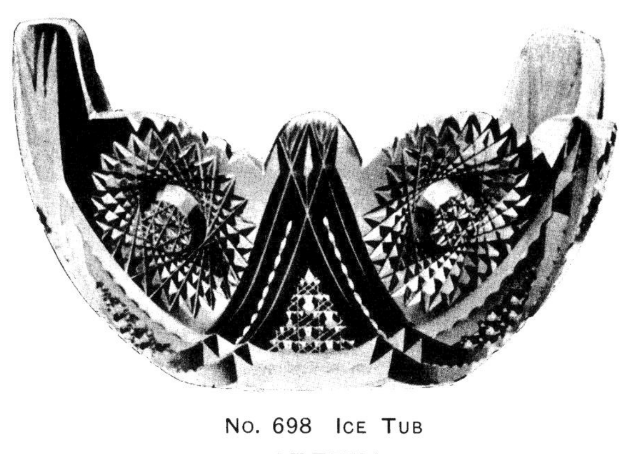

No. 698 Ice Tub
ALLITA

Two-Handled Straight Ice Tub
NARADA

No. 141 Ice Tub
SYLPH

	SYLPH	PRISM	NARADA	SATELLITE	NORMA	COMET
W. M. Jug, ½ Pint . . . . each	$7.50	. . . .	. . . .	$ 6.00	. . . .	. . . .
W. M. Jug, 2 Pint . . . . each	. . . .	. . . .	. . . .	10.50	. . . .	$ 9.50
W. M. Jug, 3 Pint . . . . each	. . . .	. . . .	. . . .	12.00	$13.00	11.50
W. M. Jug, 2 Quart . . . . each	. . . .	. . . .	. . . .	. . . .	14.00	. . . .
Straight Tankard, 1 Pint . . . . each	. . . .	. . . .	$ 9.00	. . . .	. . . .	. . . .
Straight Tankard, 2 Pint . . . . each	. . . .	. . . .	11.50	. . . .	. . . .	. . . .
Straight Tankard, 2 Quart . . . . each	. . . .	. . . .	15.00	. . . .	. . . .	. . . .
No. 886 Tankard, 2 Pint . . . . each	. . . .	$13.00	. . . .	. . . .	. . .	. . . .

W. M. ½ Pint Cream Jug
SYLPH

2 Quart W. M. Jug
NORMA

2 Quart Tankard
NARADA

No. 886 Quart Tankard
PRISM

Quart W. M. Jug
SATELLITE

	ARIEL	NARADA	SATELLITE	NORMA	COMET
W. M. Jug, 3 Pints . . . . each	. . . .	. . . .	$12.00	$13.00	$11.50
No. 456 Jug, Quart . . . . each	$13.00	. . . .	. . . .	. . . .	. . . .
No. 207 Champagne Jug, 2 Quarts . . . . each	. . . .	$20.00	. . . .	. . . .	. . . .

3-Pint W. M. Jug
COMET

No. 207 2-Quart Champagne Jug
NARADA

No. 456 Quart Jug
ARIEL

Starlight Pattern, Patented May 13, 1902.

	ARIEL	SYLPH	STARLIGHT	COMET	ALLITA
No. 1330 No-Handle Decanter, Quart . . . . each	. . . .	$16.00	$15.00	$12.00	. . . .
No. 1330 Handled Decanter, Quart . . . . each	. . . .	18.00	17.00	15.00	. . . .
No. 886 No-Handle Decanter, Quart . . . . each	$16.00	. . . .	. . . .	. . . .	. . . .
No. 886 Handled Decanter, Quart . . . . each	18.00	. . . .	. . . .	. . . .	. . . .
No. 886 Handled Decanter, ½ Pint . . . . each	12.00	. . . .	. . . .	. . . .	. . . .
Yacht Whiskey Jug . . . . each	. . . .	18.00	. . .	. . . .	. . . .
No. 520 Whiskey Tumbler . . . . dozen	. . . .	27.00	. . . .	18.00	$26.00

No. 520 Whiskey Tumbler
SYLPH

No. 1330 Quart Decanter
STARLIGHT

No. 886 Quart Decanter
ARIEL

No. 1330 Quart Decanter
COMET

Quart Yacht Whiskey Jug
SYLPH

Starlight Pattern, Patented May 13, 1902.

	ALLITA	SYLPH	STARLIGHT	COMET	NORMA
No. 530 Handled Decanter, Quart . . . . each	. . . .	$17.50	. . . .	. . . .	. . . .
No. 530 No-Handle Decanter, Quart . . . . each	. . . .	15.50	. . . .	. . . .	. . . .
No. 1330 Handled Decanter, Quart . . . . each	. . . .	18.00	$17.00	$15.00	. . . .
No. 1330 No-Handle Decanter, Quart . . . . each	. . . .	16.00	15.00	12 00	. . . .
No. 520 Whiskey Tumbler . . . . dozen	$26.00	27.00	. . . .	18.00	. . . .
No. 1730 Whiskey Jug, Quart . . . . each	15.00	. . . .	. . . .	. . . .	$12.00

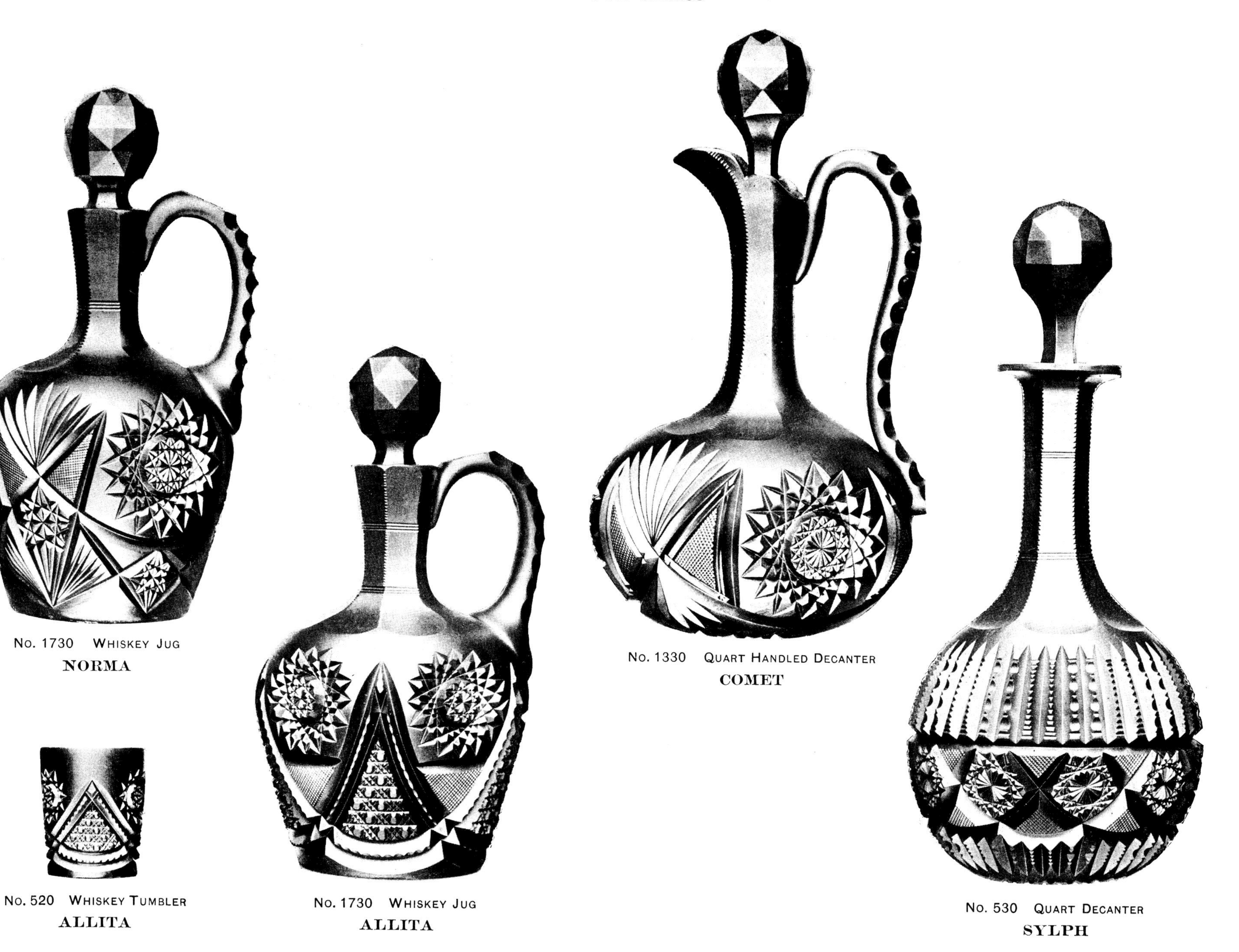

No. 1730 Whiskey Jug
NORMA

No. 520 Whiskey Tumbler
ALLITA

No. 1730 Whiskey Jug
ALLITA

No. 1330 Quart Handled Decanter
COMET

No. 530 Quart Decanter
SYLPH

	SYLPH	OLGA	SATELLITE	COMET	NORMA
No. 300 Sugar . . . . each	$6.50	. . . .	. . . .	. . . .	. . . .
No. 300 Cream . . . . each	7.50	. . . .	. . . .	. . . .	. . . .
No. 1230 Sugar and Cream . . . . set	. . . .	. . . .	. . . .	$7.00	. . . .
No. 220 Sugar and Cream . . . . set	. . . .	. . . .	. . . .	. . . .	$6.00
No. 120 Sugar and Cream . . . . set	. . . .	$13.50	$9.00	. . . .	. . . .

No. 120 Sugar
OLGA

No. 120 Cream
OLGA

No. 220 Sugar
NORMA

No. 220 Cream
NORMA

No. 300 Sugar
SYLPH

No. 300 Cream
SYLPH

No. 120 Sugar
SATELLITE

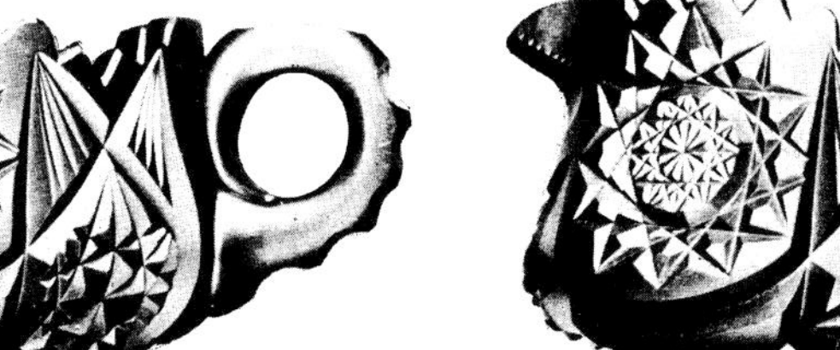

No. 120 Cream
SATELLITE

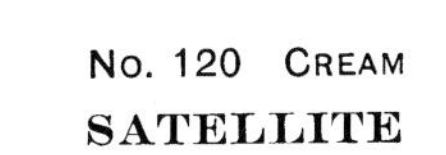

No. 1230 Sugar
COMET

No. 1230 Cream
COMET

			SYLPH
No. 527	Goblet	dozen	$56.00
No. 527	Saucer Champagne	dozen	54.00
No. 527	Claret	dozen	48 00
No. 527	Sherry	dozen	46.00
No. 527	Wine	dozen	43.00
No. 527	Cordial	dozen	40.00
No. 520	Tumbler, ½ Pint	dozen	36.00
No. 520	Apollinaris	dozen	30.00
No. 520	Lemonade	dozen	27.00
No. 520	Whiskey Tumbler	dozen	27.00
No. 520	Finger Bowl	dozen	48 00

No. 527 Goblet
SYLPH

No. 527 Champagne
SYLPH

No. 527 Claret
SYLPH

No. 527 Sherry
SYLPH

No. 527 Wine
SYLPH

No. 527 Cordial
SYLPH

No. 520 Finger Bowl
SYLPH

No. 520 ½ Pint Tumbler
SYLPH

No. 520 Apollinaris
SYLPH

No. 520 Lemonade
SYLPH

No. 520 Whiskey Tumbler
SYLPH

Starlight Pattern, Patented May 13, 1902.

			STARLIGHT
No. 730	Goblet	dozen	$40.00
No. 730	Champagne	dozen	33.00
No. 730	Claret	dozen	27.00
No. 730	Sherry	dozen	28.00
No. 730	Wine	dozen	24.00
No. 730	Cordial	dozen	21.00
No. 730	Lemonade	dozen	32.00
No. 730	½ Pint Tumbler	dozen	30.00
No. 730	Whiskey Tumbler	dozen	18.00
No. 730	Finger Bowl	each	4.00
No. 730	Plate for Finger Bowl	each	4.50

No. 730 Goblet
STARLIGHT

No. 730 Champagne
STARLIGHT

No. 730 Claret
STARLIGHT

No. 730 Sherry
STARLIGHT

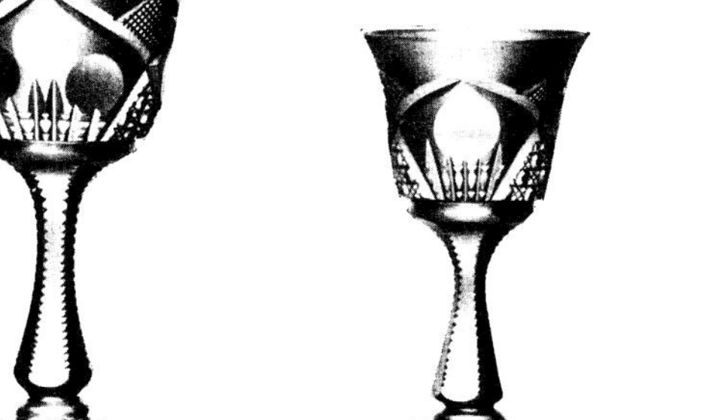

No. 730 Wine
STARLIGHT

No. 730 Cordial
STARLIGHT

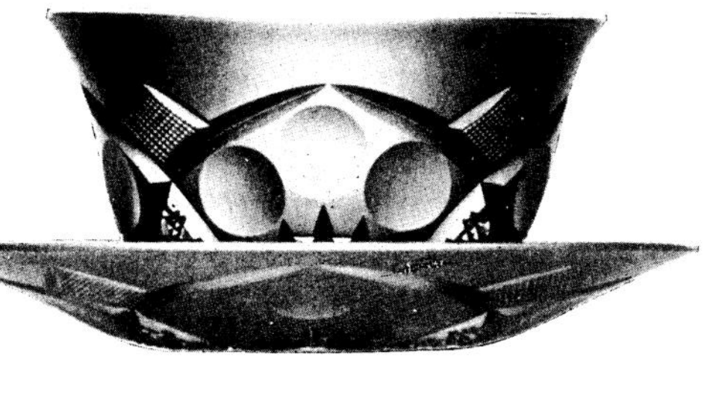

No. 730 Finger Bowl and Plate
STARLIGHT

No. 730 Lemonade
STARLIGHT

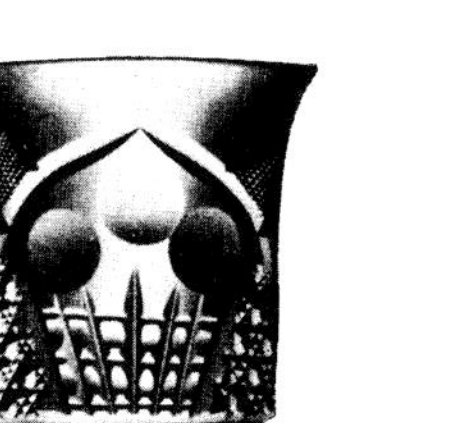

No. 730 Whiskey Tumbler
STARLIGHT

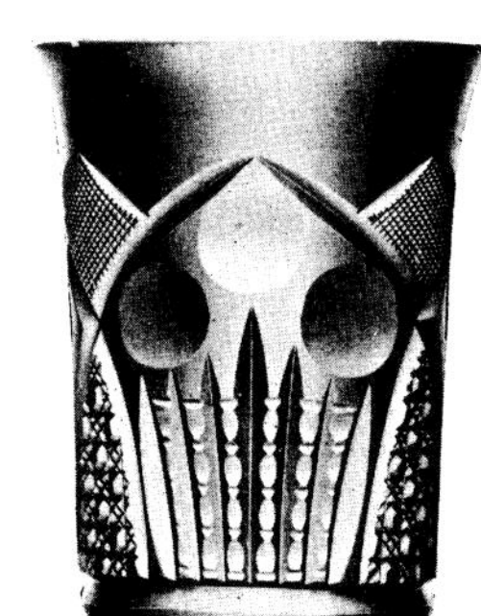

No. 730 ½ Pint Tumbler
STARLIGHT

	SATELLITE	NORMA	COMET
No. 730 Goblet . . . . . dozen	. . . . .	$36.00	. . . . .
No. 730 Champagne . . . . . dozen	. . . . .	36.00	. . . . .
No. 730 Claret . . . . . dozen	. . . . .	25.00	. . . . .
No. 730 Sherry . . . . . dozen	. . . . .	27.00	. . . . .
No. 730 Wine . . . . . dozen	. . . . .	24.00	. . . . .
No. 730 Cordial . . . . . dozen	. . . . .	20.00	. . . . .
No. 730 Lemonade . . . . . dozen	$22.00	24.00	. . . . .
No. 730 Apollinaris . . . . . dozen	. . . . .	24.00	. . . . .
No. 730 Whiskey Tumbler . . . . . dozen	. . . . .	20.00	. . . . .
No. 730 Finger Bowl . . . . . dozen	. . . . .	30.00	$24.00

No. 730 GOBLET
NORMA

No. 730 CHAMPAGNE
NORMA

No. 730 CLARET
NORMA

No. 730 SHERRY
NORMA

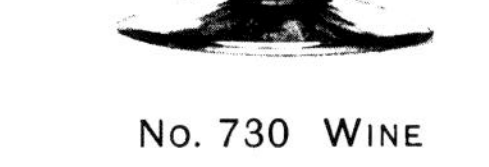

No. 730 WINE
NORMA

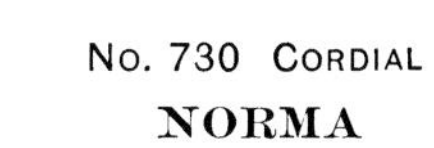

No. 730 CORDIAL
NORMA

No. 730 WHISKEY TUMBLER
NORMA

No. 730 APOLLINARIS
NORMA

No. 730 LEMONADE
NORMA

No. 730 FINGER BOWL
NORMA

No. 730 LEMONADE
SATELLITE

No. 730 FINGER BOWL
COMET

			COMET
No. 520	Goblet	dozen	$32.00
No. 520	Champagne	dozen	31.00
No. 520	Claret	dozen	25.00
No. 520	Sherry	dozen	23.00
No. 520	Wine	dozen	23.00
No. 520	Cordial	dozen	19.00
No. 520	Lemonade	dozen	18.00
No. 520	Whiskey Tumbler	dozen	18.00
No. 520	½-Pint Tumbler	dozen	24.00
No. 520	Finger Bowl	dozen	24.00
S. S. Bell		each	3.00

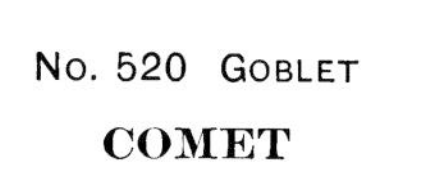

No. 520 Goblet
COMET

No. 520 Champagne
COMET

No. 520 Claret
COMET

No. 520 Sherry
COMET

No. 520 Wine
COMET

No. 520 Cordial
COMET

S. S. Bell
COMET

No. 520 Finger Bowl
COMET

No. 520 Lemonade
COMET

No. 520 Whiskey Tumbler
COMET

No. 520 ½ Pint Tumbler
COMET

	ARIEL	M-2	M-3	M-4	M-5	SATELLITE	COMET
No. 3 Cigar Jar Height, 9½ Inches . . . . each	$18.00	. . . .	. . .	. . . .	. . . .	. . . .	. . . .
No. 4 Cigar Jar Height, 9¼ Inches . . . . each	12.00	. . . .	. . . .	. . . .	. . . .	. . . .	. . . .
No. 4 Tobacco Jar Height, 8 Inches . . . each	11.00	. . . .	. . . .	. . . .	. . . .	. . . .	. . . .
½-Pint Tumblers . . . . dozen	. . . .	$7 00	$9.00	$15.00	$20.00	. . . .	. . . .
½-Pint Tumblers No. 176 . . . . dozen	. . . .	. . . .	. . . .	. . . .	. . . .	$20 00	$19.00

M-2 TUMBLER

M-3 TUMBLER

M-4 TUMBLER

M-5 TUMBLER

NO. 4 CIGAR JAR (MEDIUM SIZE)
ARIEL

NO. 176 ½ PINT TUMBLER
SATELLITE

11½ Inch Pillar Vase	each	$3.75
8½ Inch Pillar Vase	each	1.50
5½ Inch Pillar Vase	each	.80
Flute Vase	each	1.25
Ink Stand "A"	each	.90
Ink Stand "B"	each	3.00

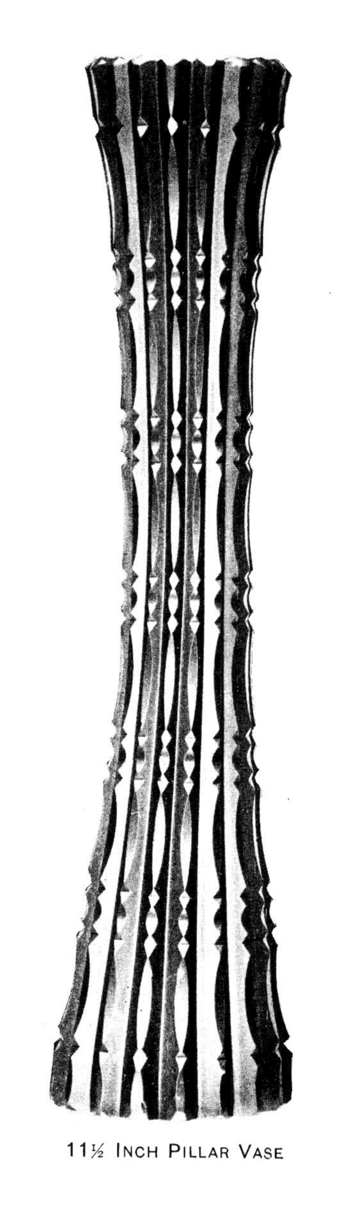

11½ Inch Pillar Vase

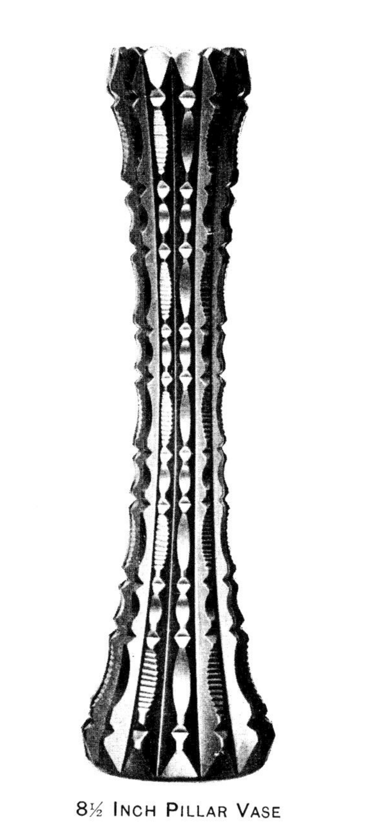

8½ Inch Pillar Vase

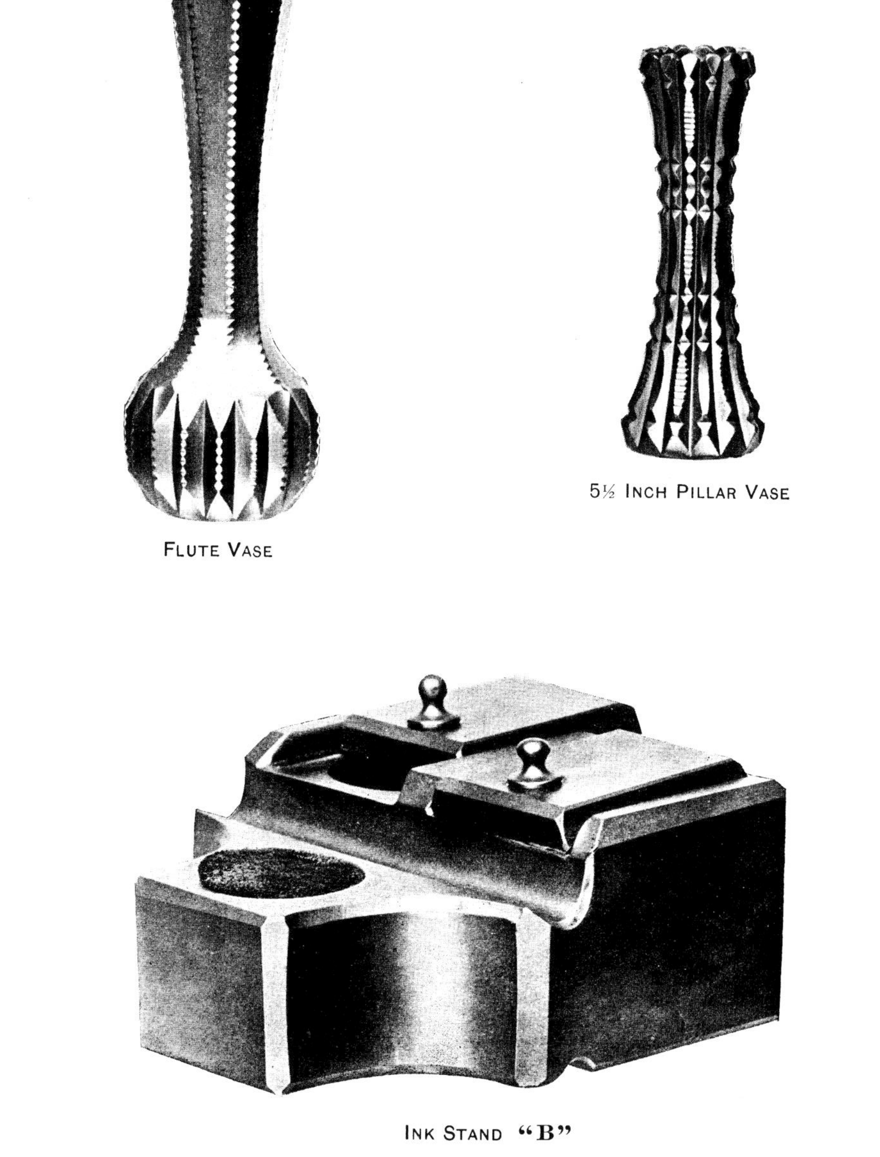

Flute Vase

5½ Inch Pillar Vase

Ink Stand "B"

Ink Stand "A"

	No. 0 Salt	No. 1 Salt	No. 3 Salt	No. 6 Salt	No. 7 Salt	No. 8 Salt	No. 9 Salt	No. 10 Salt	Square Open Salt	Round Open Salt	Oval Open Salt	Toothpick	Round Knife Rest	Square Knife Rest	Mustard
List per Dozen	$6.00	$5.00	$12.00	$5.00	$6.50	$9.00	$10.00	$6.50	$3.50	$3.50	$3.50	$4.70	$9.00	$6.00	$15.00

Cut Glass Salts, Single Screw, Sterling Silver Tops

Heavier Grade Sterling Silver Tops, list per dozen . . . . $1.00 extra

Extra Heavy Grade Sterling Silver Tops, list per dozen . . . . 2.00 extra

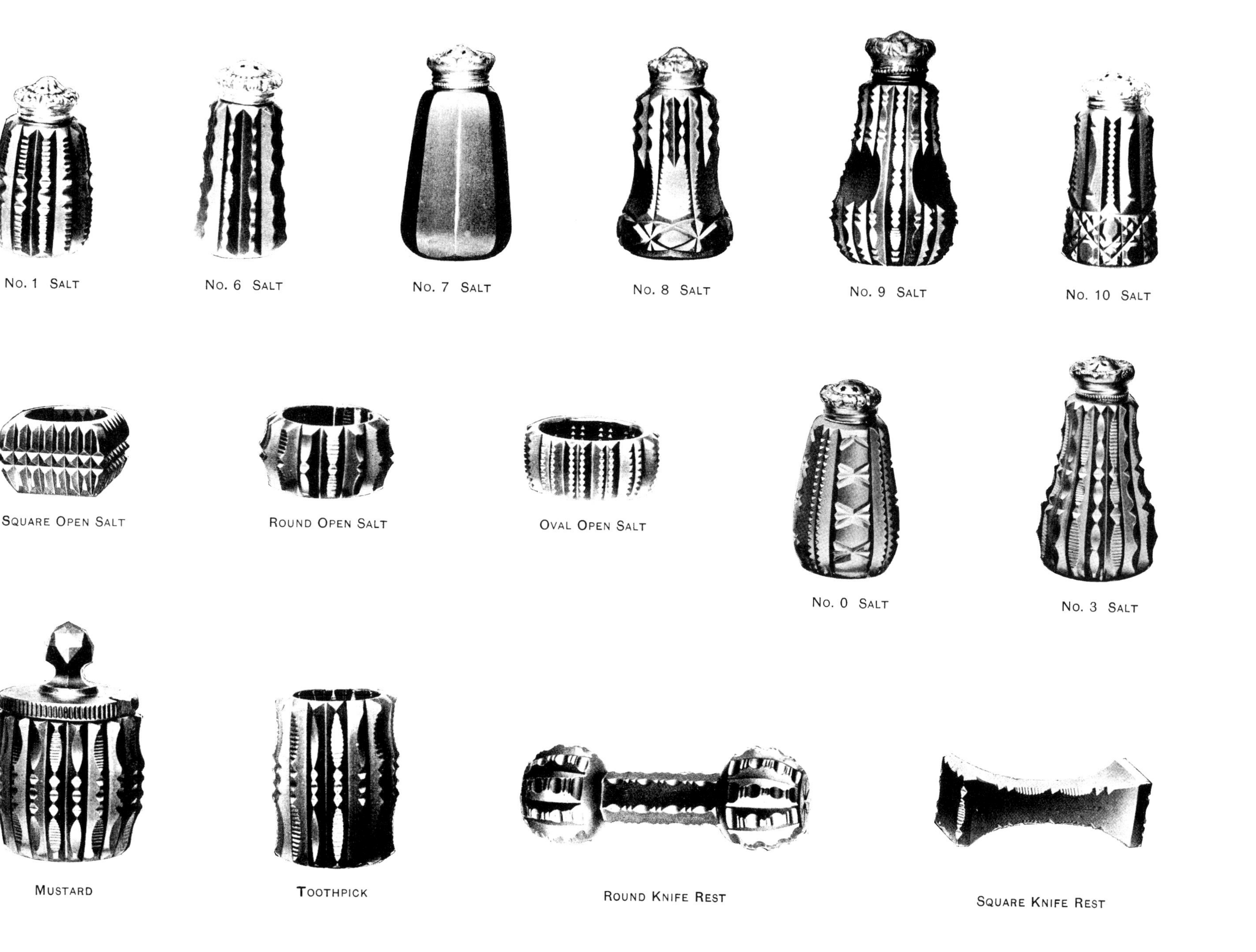

No. 1 SALT

No. 6 SALT

No. 7 SALT

No. 8 SALT

No. 9 SALT

No. 10 SALT

SQUARE OPEN SALT

ROUND OPEN SALT

OVAL OPEN SALT

No. 0 SALT

No. 3 SALT

MUSTARD

TOOTHPICK

ROUND KNIFE REST

SQUARE KNIFE REST

CATALOGUE NO. 8. 1902-1903.

WAVE CREST GEMS
WEDDING & HOLIDAY NOVELTIES.

OFFICE AND FACTORY,
MERIDEN, CONN.

NEW YORK SALESROOM,
28 BARCLAY ST.

WAVE CREST GEMS.

To the Trade:

We have to offer you this year, one of the most striking novelties on the market, which is destined to become as popular as the famous **WAVE CREST WARE** manufactured by us. The trimmings are all of 24 carat gold plate, and the finish and workmanship of the best, the decorations being hand painted and of numerous designs to meet the tastes of all.

Get your orders in first and reap the benefit. Do not wait until it has been used four or five years, and then hearing it has been a winner, fall in at the tail end of the line and begin to purchase.

You all know what our **WAVE CREST WARE** is. It is claimed by the trade in general that it is the most wonderful line ever put on the market, and we believe these **GEMS** are equal in every respect. They certainly are new.

WAVE CREST WARE.

It is needless for us to expatiate on our general line We have made many changes and additions this year, reducing the prices quite a little on the highest grade goods only, trying to make them more within the reach of the masses. The workmanship will still retain the highest merit.

Having made no attempt to give the decorations, it being impossible to show the difference between an article of one price and that of another, we have therefore illustrated the shapes only. Goods manufactured by us are known the country over and our reputation is second to none. The same thing applies to our **CUT GLASS** ware of which we illustrate another complete catalogue, showing a most beautiful line. It can be had on application.

Instructions for Ordering.

When ordering, mention first the number and letter under the article, then the number of Assortment. For example, if you wanted the Mirror Tray on page 30, for $12.00 list, write the order thus: 264—F. Z. Assortment 6. This rule follows through the catalogue. The first numbers always mean the article. The letters, the kind of trimming, and the assortment number denotes the grade of finish.

Goods billed F. O. B Meriden, and a charge made for all packages, this last item not being reckoned in the cost of our wares. Cash discounts forfeited if not paid within time limit.

Address all communications to Factory, Meriden, Conn., U. S. A.

All orders and correspondence should be written on one side of paper only.

Description of Assortments.

Assortment 1, consists of Decorations on White Ground, Glazed.
Assortment 2, consists of Decorations on Tinted Ground, Glazed.
Assortment 2½, consists of Decorations on Tinted Ground, Fire Bisque Finish.
Assortment 3, consists of Decorations on Tinted Ground, Glazed, designs more elaborate
Assortment 4, consists of Decorations on Tinted Ground, Bisque Finish.
Assortment 5, consists of Decorations on Tinted Ground, Bisque Finish, designs traced in gold.
Assortment 6, consists of Decorations, traced in gold, very elegant and striking.

THE C. F. MONROE CO.,

MANUFACTURERS OF

Wedding and Holiday Novelties.

NEW YORK SALESROOMS,
28 Barclay St., U. S. A.
Telephone Call 6973 A, Courtlandt.

MAIN OFFICE AND FACTORY,
Meriden, Conn., U. S. A.

DISPLAYING WAVE CREST WARE.

The following is merely a suggestion:

Naturally we would be pleased to have all of our wares displayed together as much as possible, for we think one materially helps the sale of the other and the contrast is very striking and pleasing, and the benefit will be mutual.

Our goods kept in a glass showcase with a box open now and then, mixing in pieces of our CUT GLASS and a few of the Gems would meet with good results.

Avoid handling all goods as much as possible, keep them clean and bright, and the stock will always be fresh and nice.

When soiled, a little soap and water will not hurt the decorations, but avoid putting it on the trimmings, as they are usually lacquered to protect the gold.

SAMPLES OF GOODS CHEERFULLY SUBMITTED.

When visiting New York, the following directions to our New York store may be of assistance:

If uptown or near the Grand Central Depot, take Sixth Ave. elevated train, get out at Park St. station, corner of Church, walk from Church St. to Barclay, one block, we are two doors from the corner.

If taking Broadway surface car, get out at Barclay St., continue down to the first cross street which is Church St.; we are two doors from same, left hand side.

If coming down Ninth Ave. elevated, get out at Barclay St. station, continue up the right hand side to 28 Barclay St.

If on the elevated cars, getting out at the bridge, cross the park to Broadway side of the Post Office; Barclay St. starts right at lower end of the Post Office on Broadway.

INDEX OF ARTICLES.

INDEX BY NUMBER.

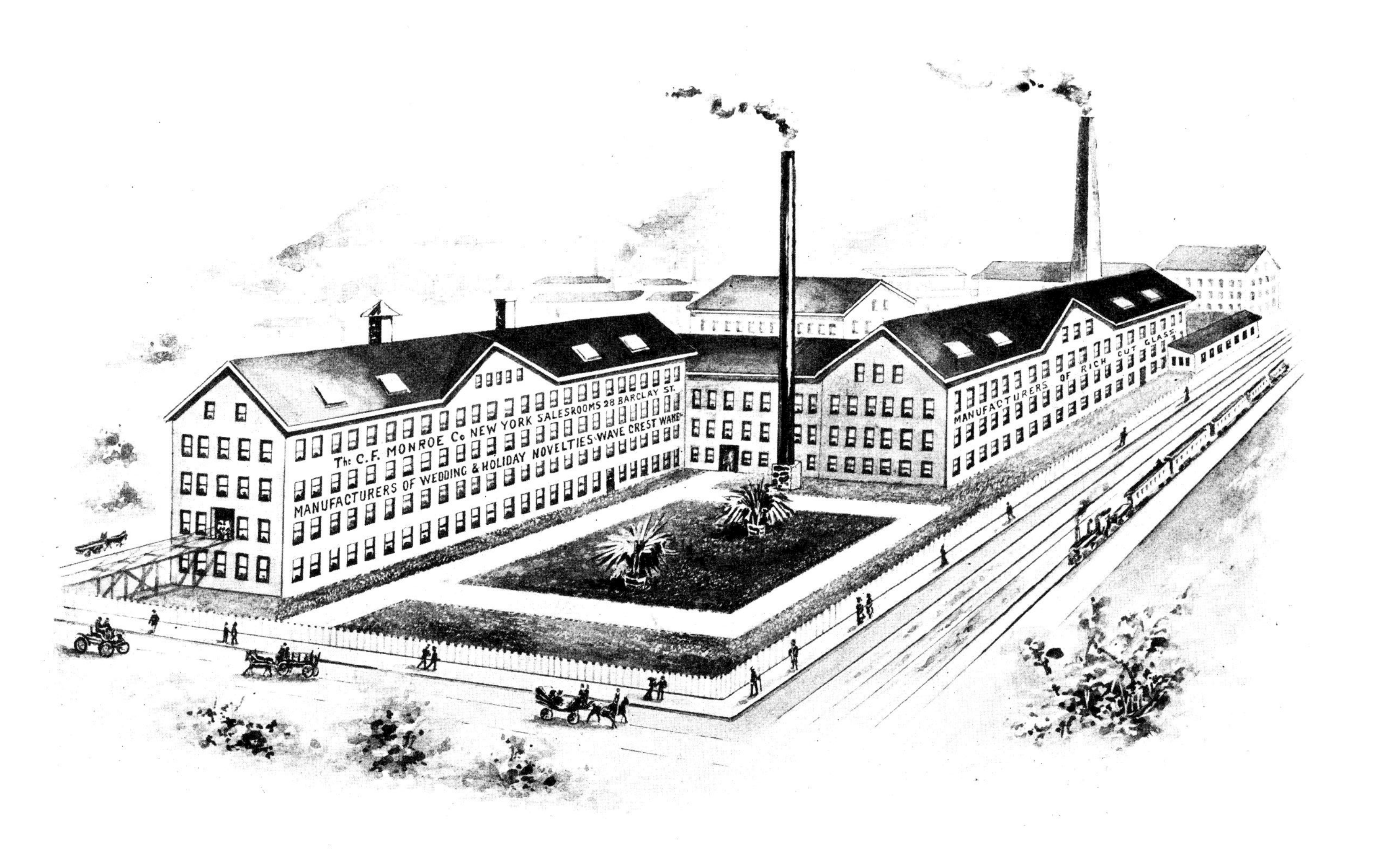

FACTORIES OF THE C. F. MONROE CO., MERIDEN, CONN.

EXTERIOR VIEW NEW YORK STORE, 28 BARCLAY STREET.

FACTORY OFFICES, MERIDEN, CONN.

FACTORY OFFICES, MERIDEN, CONN.

INTERIOR VIEW OF OUR NEW YORK STORE, 28 BARCLAY STREET.

WAVE CREST GEMS.

BEAUTIFUL DESIGNS.

FRAMES 24 CARAT GOLD PLATE.

DIAMETER, 10 INCHES.

Cuts about one-third actual size.

Gem No. 5, list each, . . . $13 50
Gem No. 3 is this Decoration mounted the same as No. 4, list each, 15.00

Gem No. 4, list each, ... $15.00
Gem No. 6 is this Decoration mounted the same as No. 5, list each, 13.50

Gem No. 1, list each, ... $17.00

WAVE CREST GEMS.

FRAMES 24 CARAT GOLD PLATE.
DIAMETER, 10 INCHES.
Cuts about one-third actual size.

Gem No. 2, list each, ... $17.00

WAVE CREST GEMS.

FRAMES 24 CARAT GOLD PLATE.
DIAMETER, 10 INCHES.
Cuts about one-third actual size.

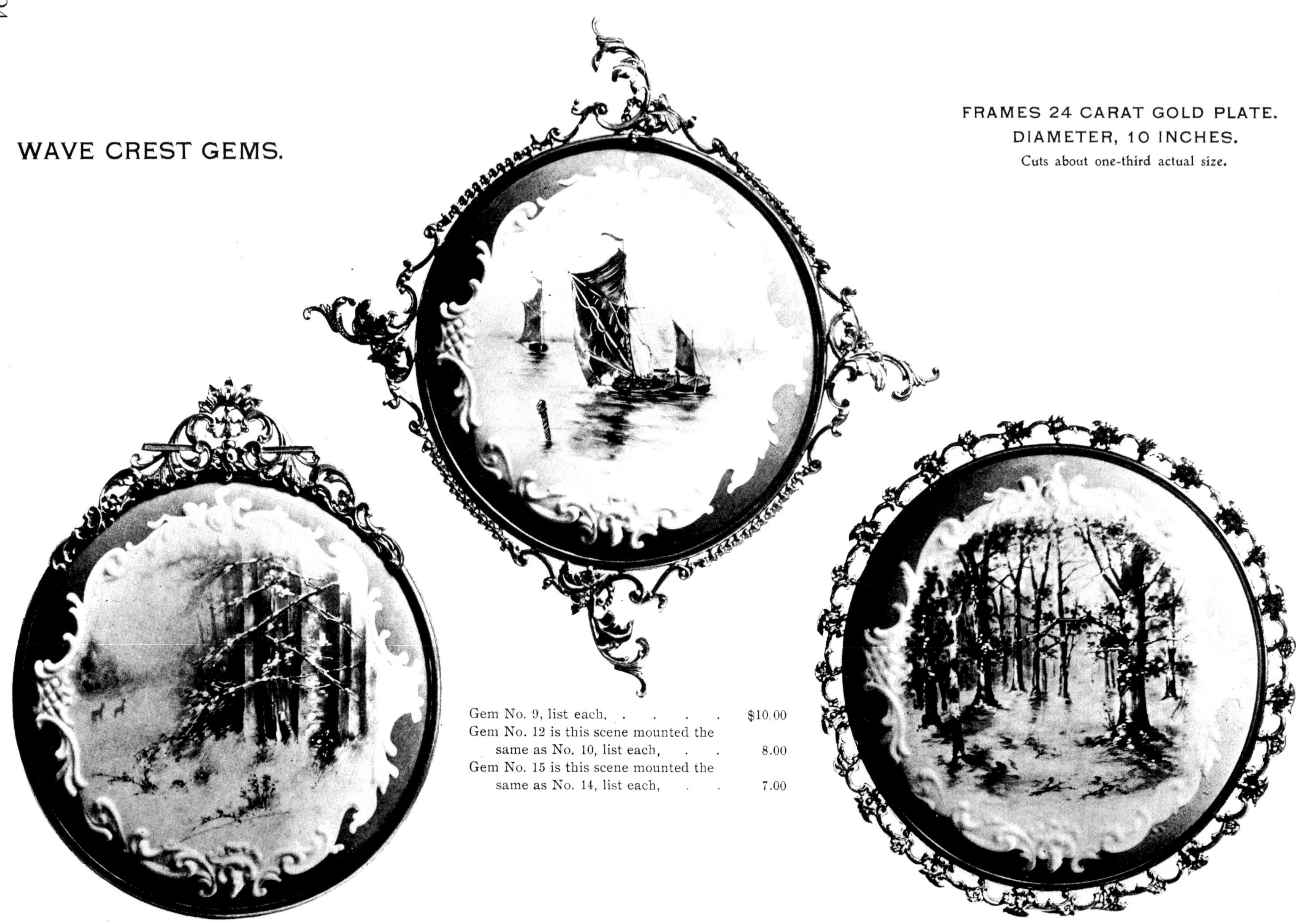

Gem No. 9, list each, ... $10.00
Gem No. 12 is this scene mounted the same as No. 10, list each, . . . 8.00
Gem No. 15 is this scene mounted the same as No. 14, list each, . . 7.00

Gem No. 14, list each, ... $7.00
Gem No. 11 is this scene mounted the same as No. 10, list each, 8.00
Gem No. 8 is this scene mounted the same as No. 9, list each, 10.00

Gem No. 10, list each, ... $8.00
Gem No. 7 is this scene mounted the same as No. 9, list each, 10.00
Gem No. 13 is this scene mounted the same as No. 14, list each, 7.00

WAVE CREST GEMS.

FRAMES 24 CARAT GOLD PLATE. DIAMETER, 10 INCHES.

Cuts about one-third actual size.

Gem No. 18, list each, ... $8 00

Gem No. 23, list each, ... $5.00
Gem No. 20 is this Decoration, mounted the same as No. 18, list each, ... 6.00

Gem No. 25, list each, ... $5.00
Gem No. 22 is this Decoration, mounted the same as No. 18, list each, ... 6.00

Gem No. 24, list each, ... $5 00
Gem No. 21 is this Decoration, mounted the same as No. 18, list each, ... 6.00

WAVE CREST GEMS.

FRAMES 24 CARAT GOLD PLATE.

Cuts about one-third actual size.

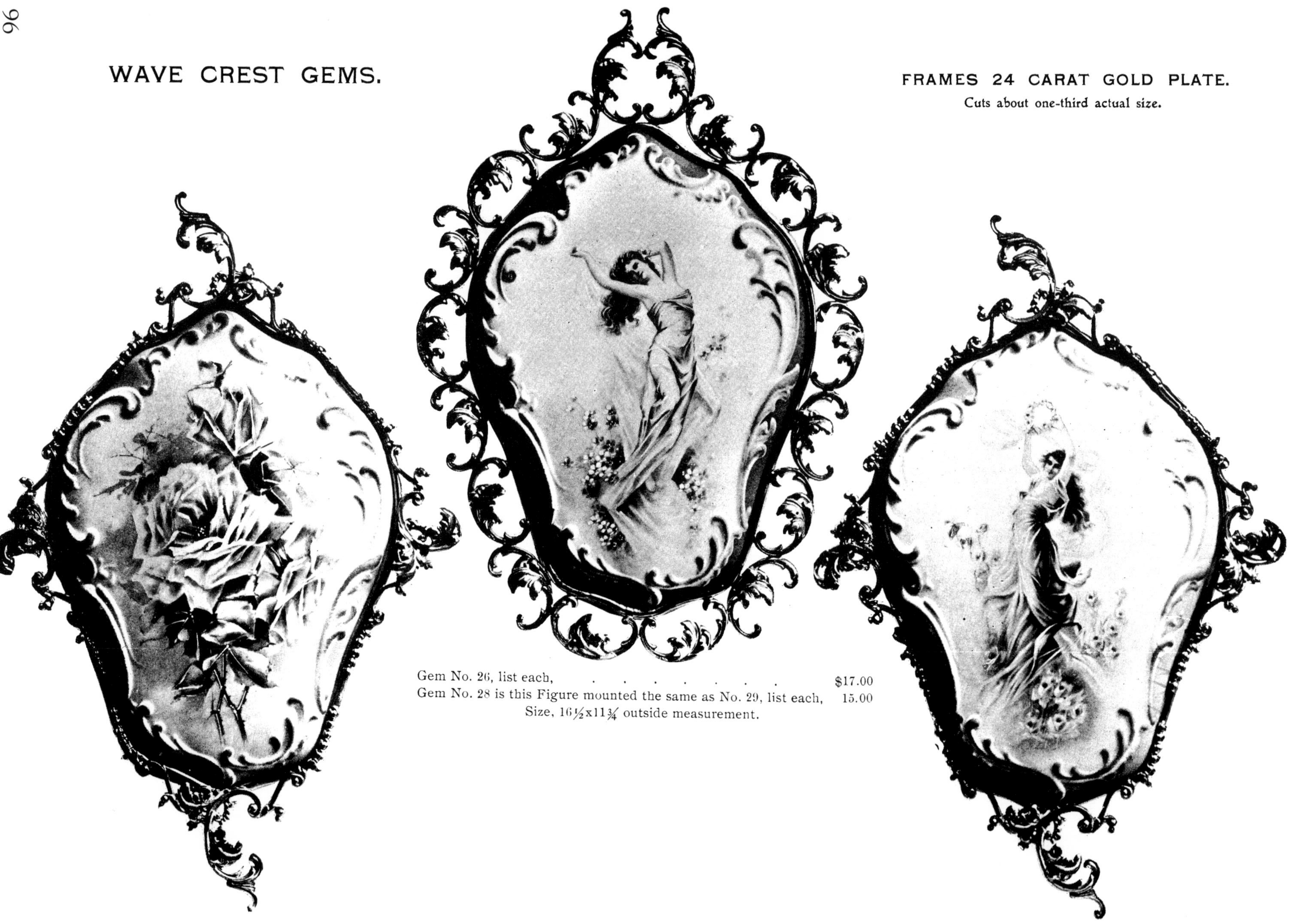

Gem No. 26, list each, ... $17.00
Gem No. 28 is this Figure mounted the same as No. 29, list each, 15.00
Size, $16\frac{1}{2}$x$11\frac{3}{4}$ outside measurement.

Gem No. 30, list each, ... $15.00
Size, $17\frac{1}{2}$x$11\frac{7}{8}$ outside measurement.

Gem No. 29, list each, ... $15.00
Gem No. 27 is this Figure mounted the same as No. 26, list each, 17.00
Size, $17\frac{1}{2}$x$11\frac{7}{8}$ outside measurement.

WAVE CREST GEMS.

FRAMES 24 CARAT GOLD PLATE.

Cuts about one-third actual size.

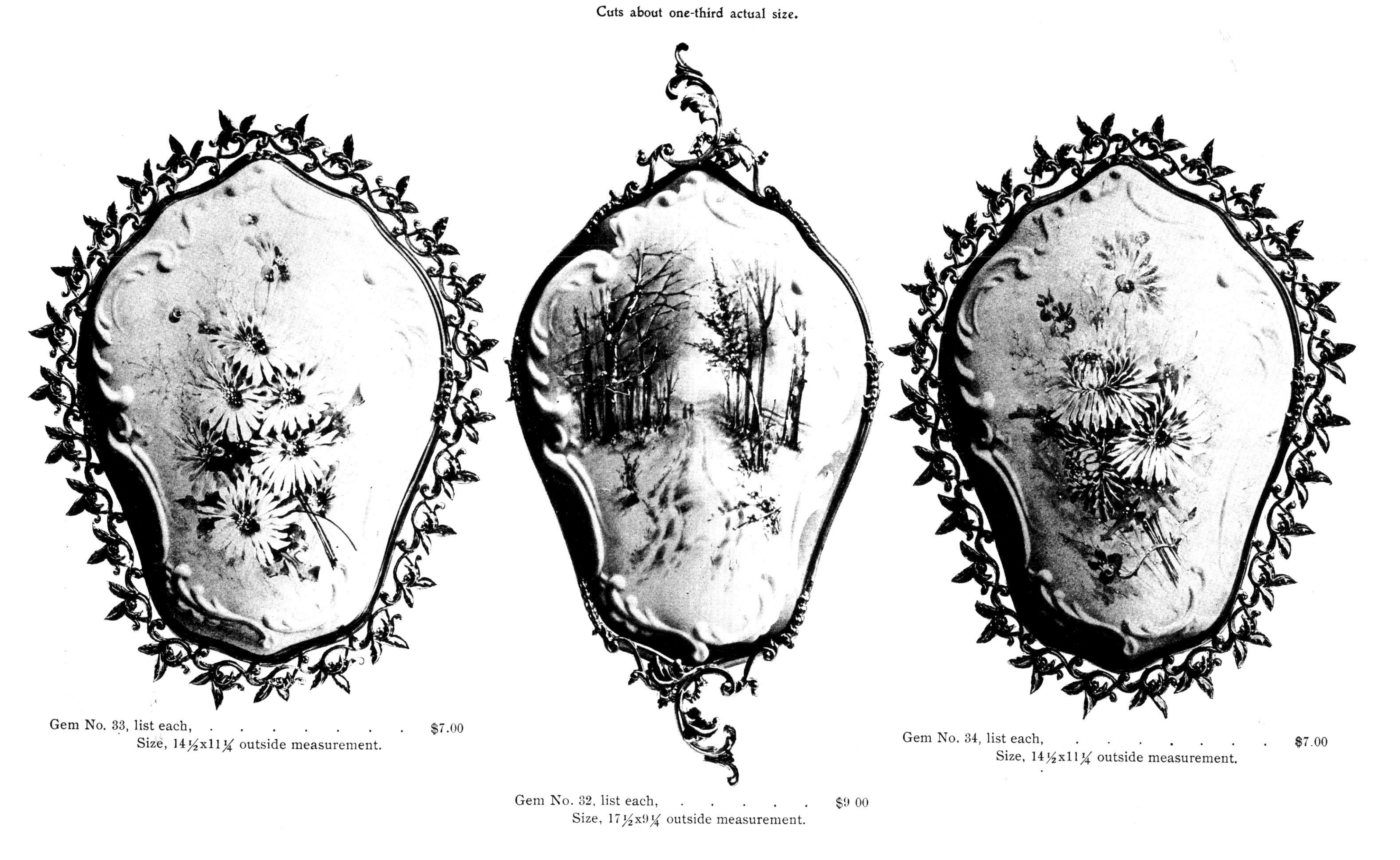

Gem No. 33, list each, ... $7.00
Size, 14½x11¼ outside measurement.

Gem No. 32, list each, ... $9 00
Size, 17½x9¼ outside measurement.

Gem No. 34, list each, ... $7.00
Size, 14½x11¼ outside measurement.

WAVE CREST GEMS.

FRAMES 24 CARAT GOLD PLATE.

Cuts about one-third actual size.

Gem No. 34½, list each, ... $7.00
Size, 14½x11¼ outside measurement.

Gem No. 31, list each, ... $12.00
Size, 17½x9¼ outside measurement.

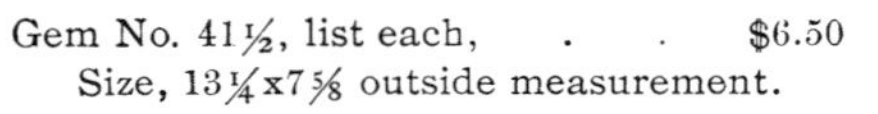

Gem No. 41½, list each, . . . $6.50
Size, 13¼x7⅝ outside measurement.

Gem No. 19, list each, ... $8.00
10 inches diameter.

WAVE CREST GEMS.

FRAMES 24 CARAT GOLD PLATE.

Size, 13¼x7⅝ outside measurement.

Cuts about one-third actual size.

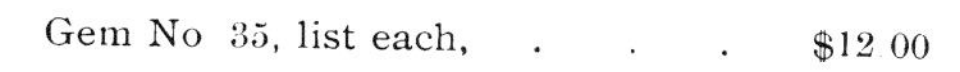

Gem No 35, list each, ... $12 00

Gem No. 36, list each, ... $8.50

Gem No. 37, list each, ... $8.50

Gem No. 38, list each, ... $8.50

WAVE CREST GEMS.

FRAMES 24 CARAT GOLD PLATE.

Size, 10½x10¾ outside measurement.

Cuts about one-third actual size.

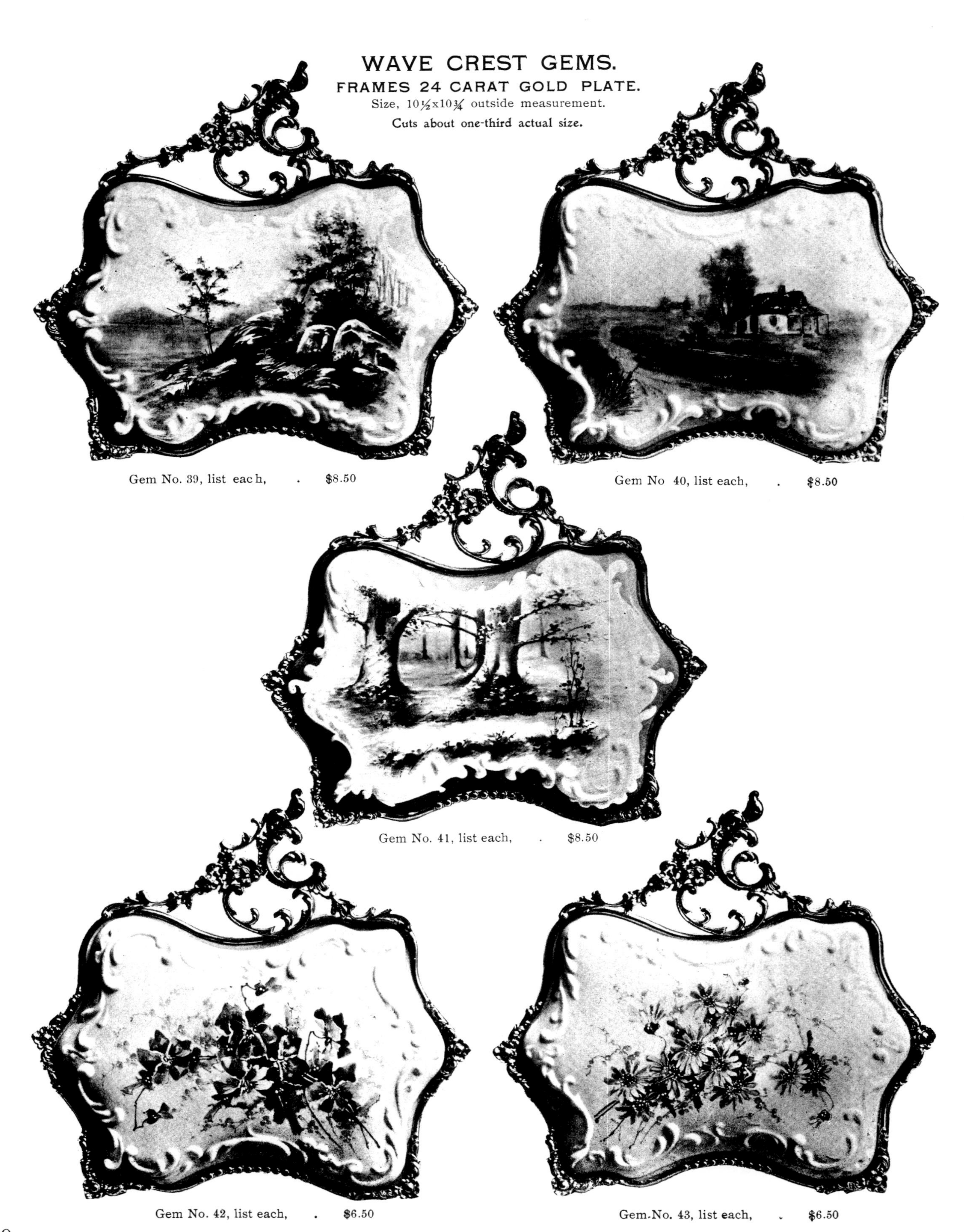

Gem No. 39, list each, . $8.50

Gem No 40, list each, . $8.50

Gem No. 41, list each, . $8.50

Gem No. 42, list each, . $6.50

Gem.No. 43, list each, . $6.50

WAVE CREST GEMS.

FRAMES 24 CARAT GOLD PLATE.

Size, 16x9 outside measurement.

Cuts about one-third actual size.

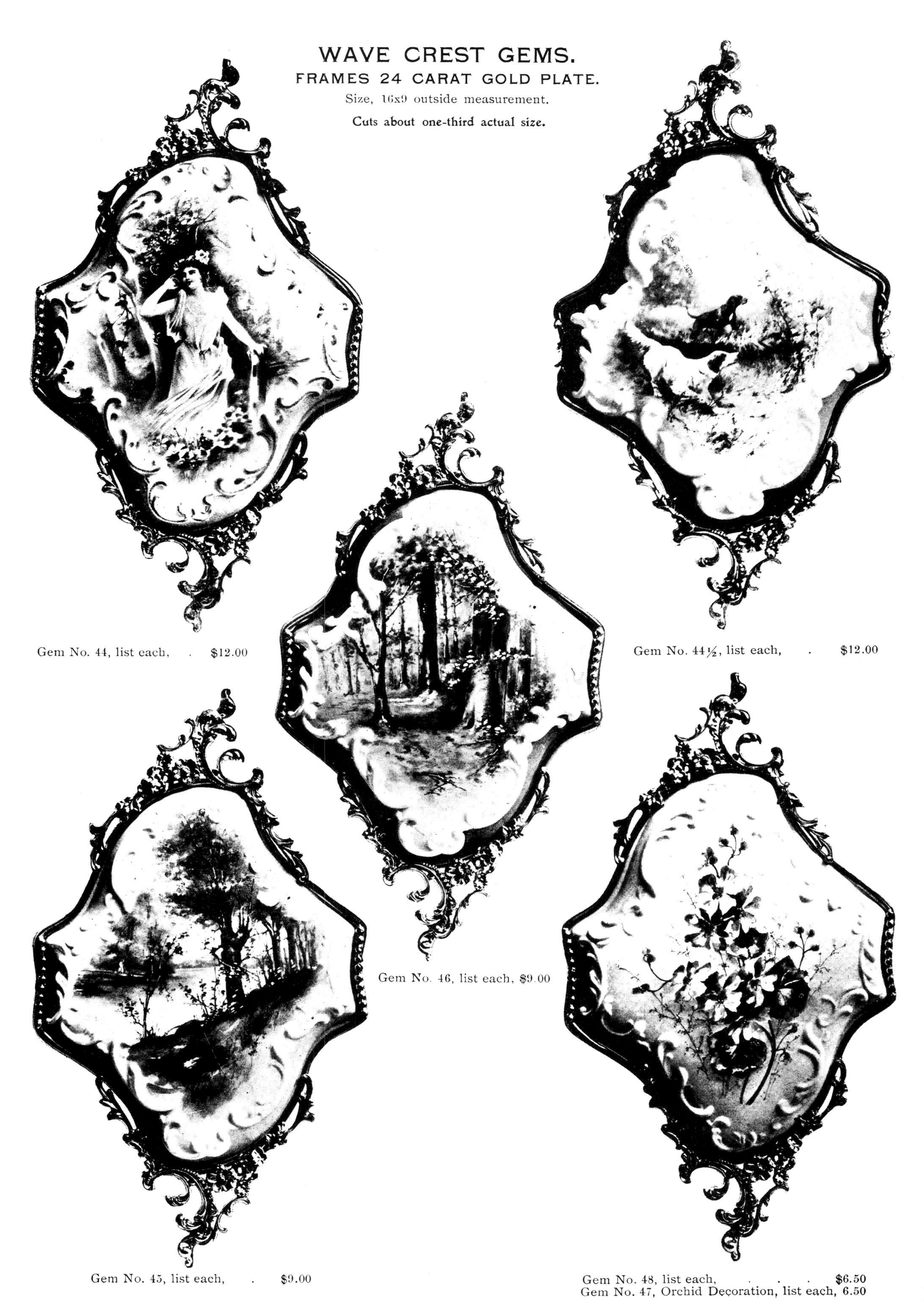

Gem No. 44, list each, . $12.00

Gem No. 44½, list each, . $12.00

Gem No. 46, list each, $9.00

Gem No. 45, list each, . $9.00

Gem No. 48, list each, . . . $6.50
Gem No. 47, Orchid Decoration, list each, 6.50

WAVE CREST GEMS.

FRAMES 24 CARAT GOLD PLATE.

Size, 12$\frac{7}{8}$x11$\frac{1}{8}$ outside measurement.

Cuts about one-third actual size.

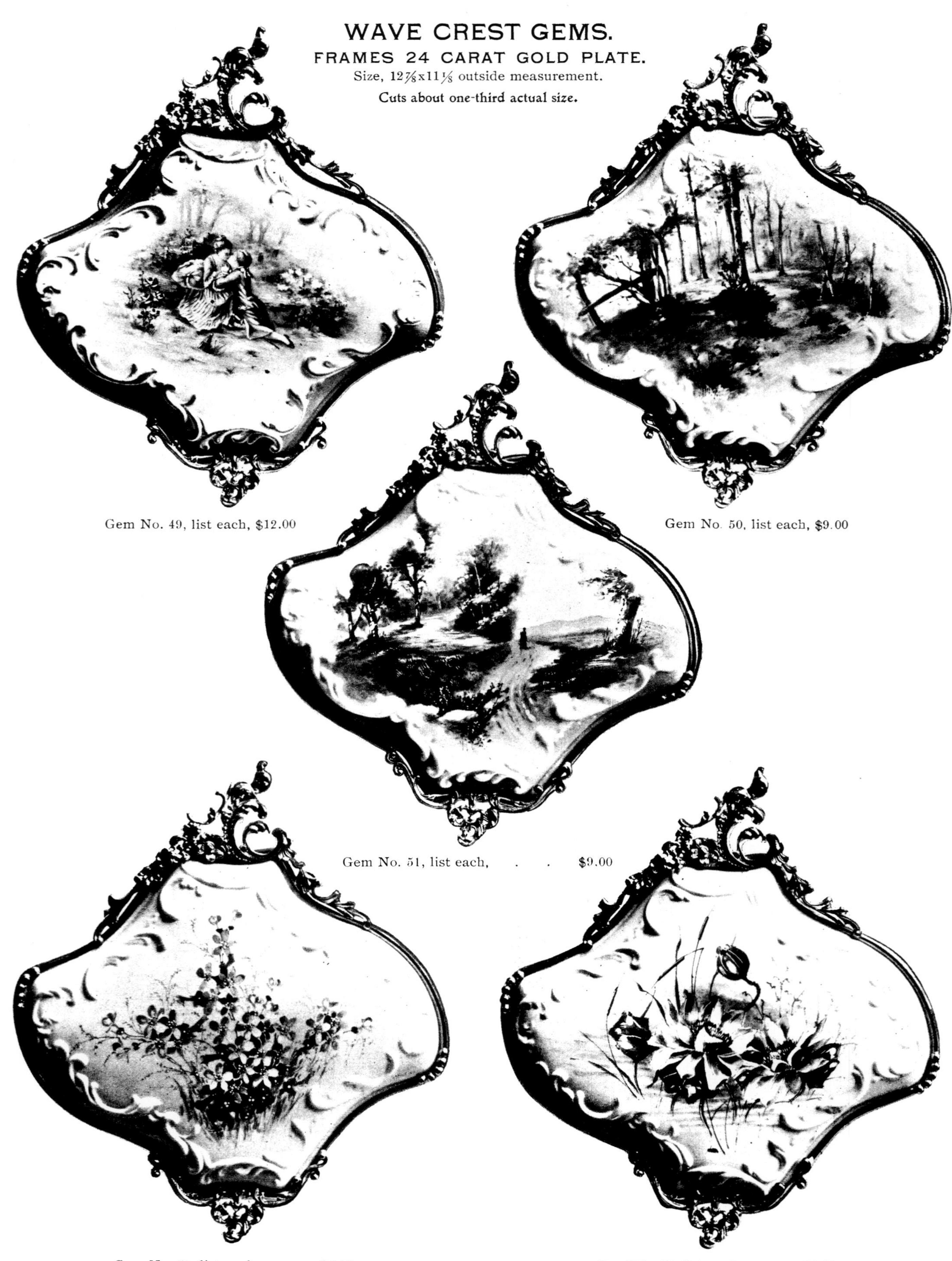

Gem No. 49, list each, $12.00

Gem No. 50, list each, $9.00

Gem No. 51, list each, . . $9.00

Gem No. 52, list each, . $6.50

Gem No. 53, list each, . $6.50

WAVE CREST GEMS.

FRAMES 24 CARAT GOLD PLATE.

Diameter, 6 inches.

Cuts about one-third actual size.

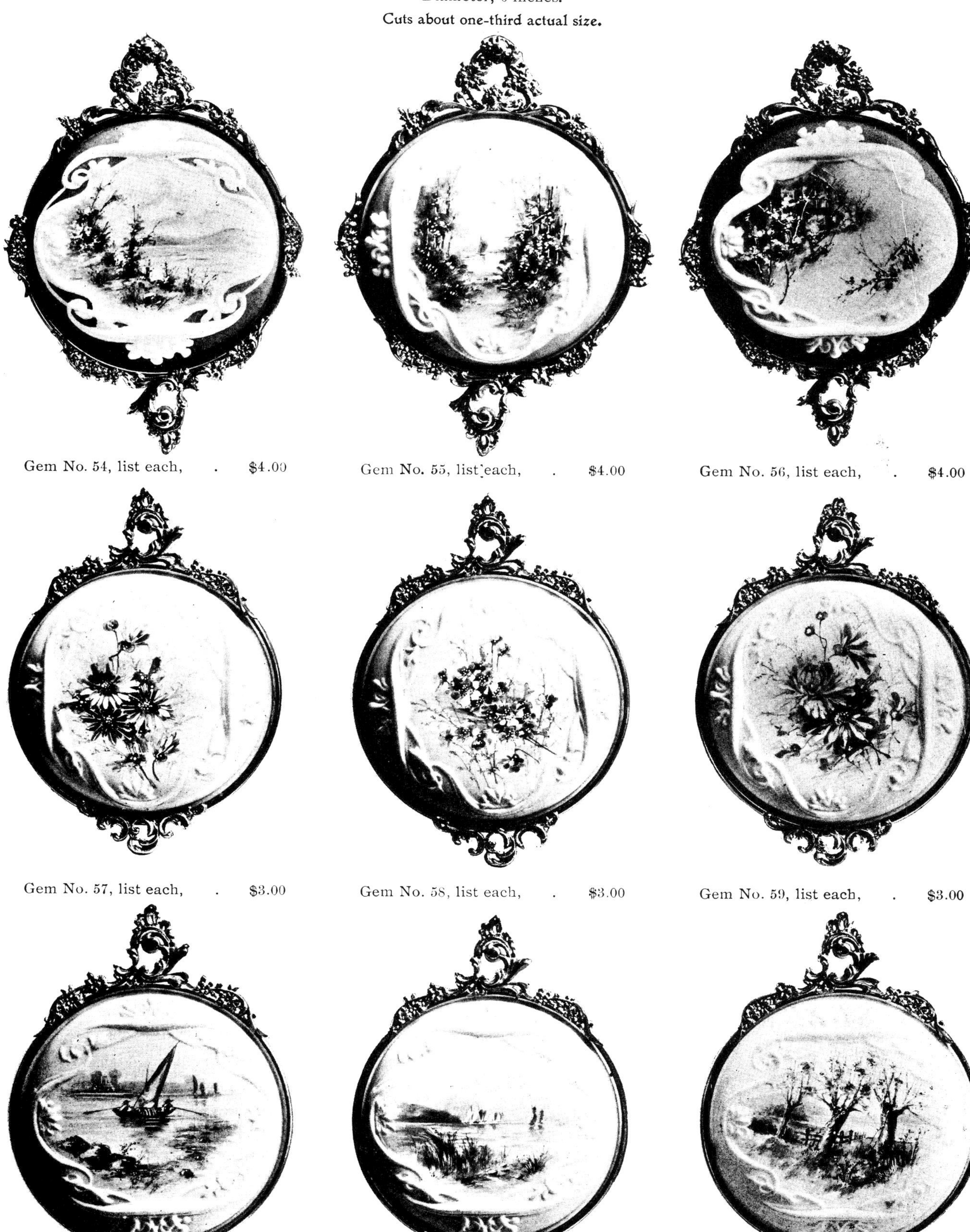

Gem No. 54, list each, . $4.00

Gem No. 55, list each, . $4.00

Gem No. 56, list each, . $4.00

Gem No. 57, list each, . $3.00

Gem No. 58, list each, . $3.00

Gem No. 59, list each, . $3.00

Gem No. 60, list each, $3.00

Gem No. 61, list each, $3.00

Gem No. 62, list each, . $3.00

WAVE CREST GEMS.

Diameter, 8 inches.

FRAMES 24 CARAT GOLD PLATE.

Cuts about one-third actual size.

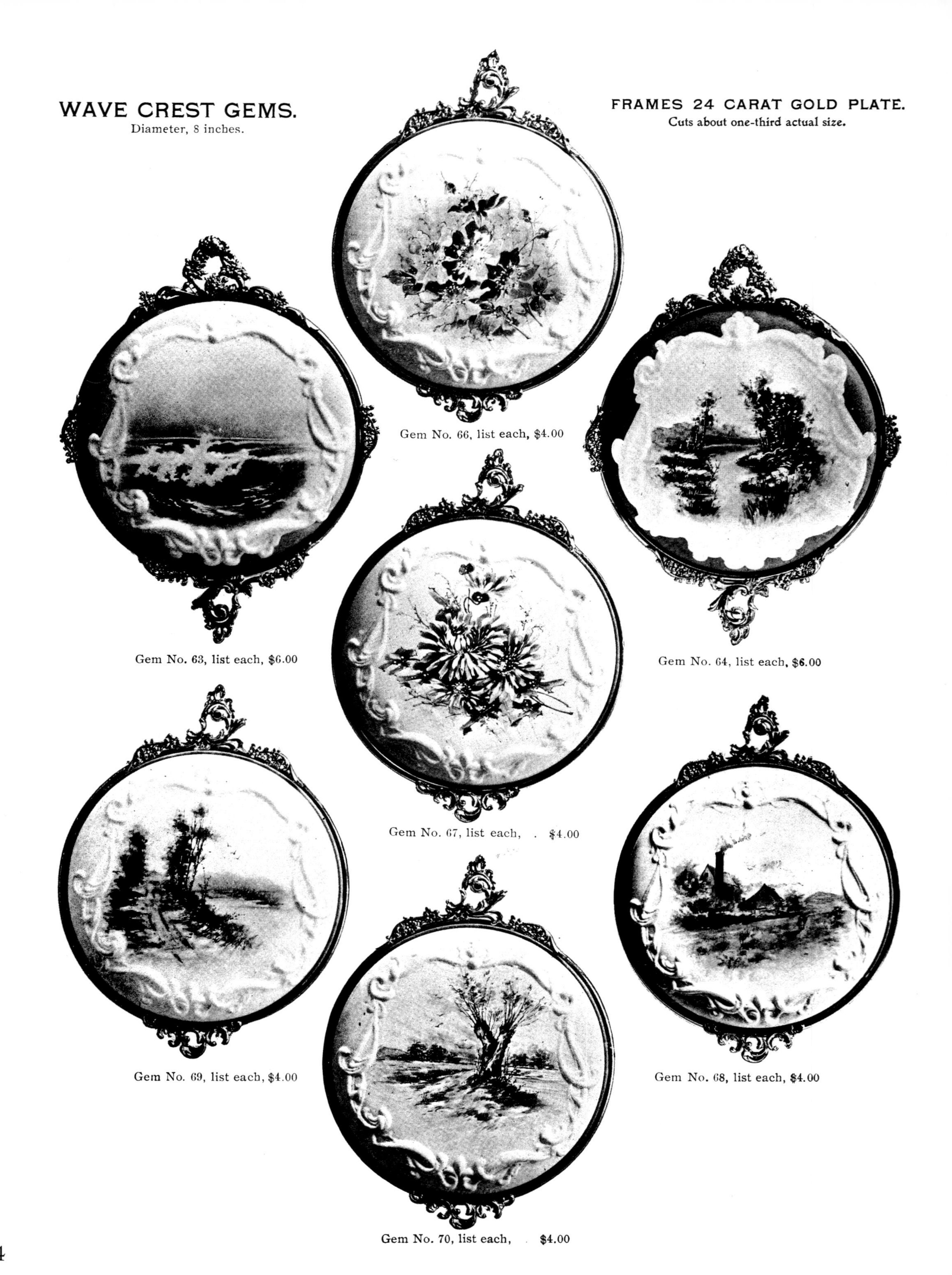

Gem No. 66, list each, $4.00

Gem No. 63, list each, $6.00

Gem No. 64, list each, $6.00

Gem No. 67, list each, . $4.00

Gem No. 69, list each, $4.00

Gem No. 68, list each, $4.00

Gem No. 70, list each, $4.00

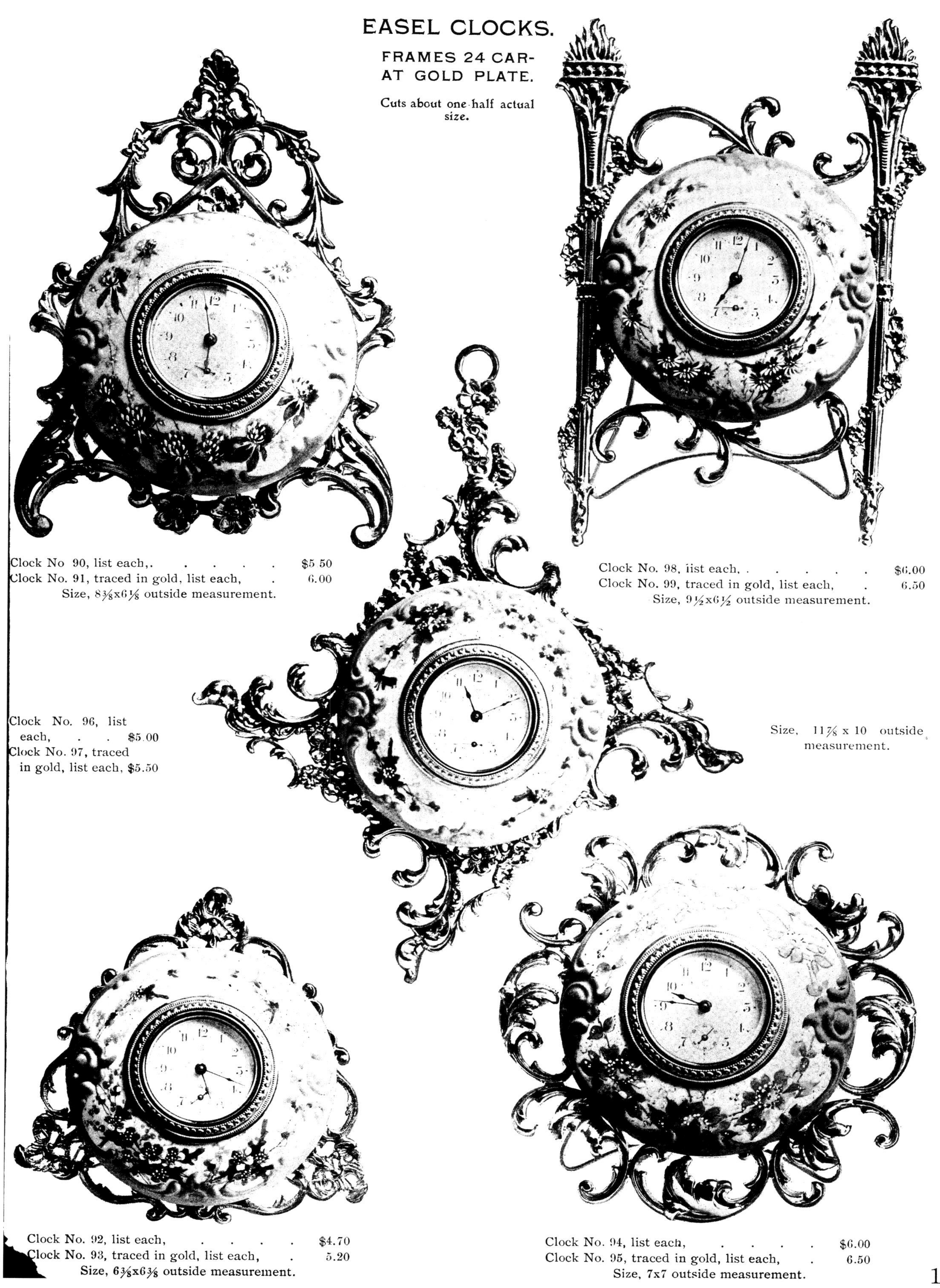

EASEL CLOCKS.

FRAMES 24 CARAT GOLD PLATE.

Cuts about one half actual size.

Clock No 90, list each,. $5 50
Clock No. 91, traced in gold, list each, . 6.00
Size, 8⅜x6⅛ outside measurement.

Clock No. 98, iist each, ... $6.00
Clock No. 99, traced in gold, list each, . 6.50
Size, 9½x6½ outside measurement.

Clock No. 96, list each, . . $5.00
Clock No. 97, traced in gold, list each, $5.50

Size, 11⅞ x 10 outside measurement.

Clock No. 92, list each, ... $4.70
Clock No. 93, traced in gold, list each, . 5.20
Size, 6⅜x6⅜ outside measurement.

Clock No. 94, list each, ... $6.00
Clock No. 95, traced in gold, list each, . 6.50
Size, 7x7 outside measurement.

WAVE CREST WARE.

Patented October 4, 1892.

This Jardiniere and Umbrella Stand makes a most attractive and useful piece of furniture Rich decorations, embossed panels, metal top of artistic design.

Cuts about one-third actual size.

Umbrella Stand without feet, list each $2.00 less for either assortment.

Jardiniere Stand 266—V L.

Assortment 1, list each, $15.00
Assortment 2½, list each, 16.00

Assortment 4, list each, $24.00
Assortment 5, list each, 30.00

Umbrella Stand 266—W L.

Assortment 1, list each, $19.00
Assortment 2½, list each, 20.00

Assortment 4, list each, $27.00
Assortment 5, list each, 32.00

WAVE CREST WARE.

Patented October 4, 1892.

This Jardiniere Stand, with its elaborately embossed and beautifully decorated panels, makes a most ornamental and useful piece of furniture. The top is of metal, artistic in design and finish.

Cut about one-third actual size.

See Page 25 for prices of Jardinieres to match Stands.

Jardiniere Stand 266—T L.

Without Jardiniere, Assortment 1, list each,	$12.00	Without Jardiniere, Assortment 4, list each,	$20.00
Without Jardiniere, Assortment 2½, list each,	13.00	Without Jardiniere, Assortment 5, list each,	27.00

WAVE CREST WARE.

Patented October 4, 1892.

OPAL JARDINIERES, DECORATED.

For Description of Assortment, see page 1.

Cuts about one-half actual size.

Jardiniere 275.

Assortment 4, list each,	. .	$3.50
Assortment 5, list each,	. .	5.50

Jardiniere 185.

Assortment 1, list each,	. .	$2.00
Assortment 2, list each,	. .	2 25
Assortment 2½, list each,	. .	2.50
Assortment 4, list each,	. .	$5.00
Assortment 5, list each,	. .	7.00
Assortment 6, list each,	. .	12.00

WAVE CREST WARE.

Patented October 4, 1892.

OPAL JARDINIERES, DECORATED.

For description of Assortments, see page 1.

Cuts about one-half actual size.

Jardiniere 50.

Assortment 1, list each,	$1.00	Assortment 2½, list each,	$1.20
Assortment 2, list each,	1.10	Assortment 4, list each,	2.00

Jardiniere 275—C Z.

Assortment 4, list each,	$6.00	Assortment 5, list each,	$8.00

This Jar having Gold Plated Top Ring and Handsomely Designed Feet makes an attractive article.

WAVE CREST WARE.

Patented October 4, 1892.

FERNERIES.

Trimmings are gold plated with detachable perforated dishes.

Cuts about one-half actual size.

Fernery 393—V S.

Assortment 4, list each, . . . $2.50

Fernery 327—V S.

Assortment 4, list each, . . . $2.50
Assortment 6, list each, . . 4.00

Fernery 213—M W.

Assortment 4, list each, . . . $3.00
Traced in Gold. Assortment 5, list each, . . 4.00

Fernery 431—W X.

Assortment 4, list each, ... $3.00

WAVE CREST WARE.

Patented October 4, 1892.

FERNERIES.

Trimmings are gold plated with detachable perforated dishes.

Cuts about one-half actual size.

Fernery 300—W X.

Assortment 4, list each, ... $3.00

Fernery 386—W X.

Assortment 4, list each, ... $3.00

Fernery 391—M W.

Assortment 4, list each, ... $3.50

Fernery 298—M W.

Assortment 4, list each, $3.00 Assortment 6, list each, $5.00

WAVE CREST WARE.

Patented October 4, 1892.

FERNERIES.

Trimmings are gold plated with detachable perforated dishes.

Cuts about one-half actual size.

Fernery 260—W X.

Assortment 4, list each, . $3.00

Fernery 300—F S

Assortment 6, list each, . . $8.00

Fernery 260—F S

Assortment 5, list each. . . $5.50

WAVE CREST WARE.

Patented October 4, 1892.

FERNERIES.

Trimmings are gold plated with detachable perforated dishes.

Cuts about one-half actual size.

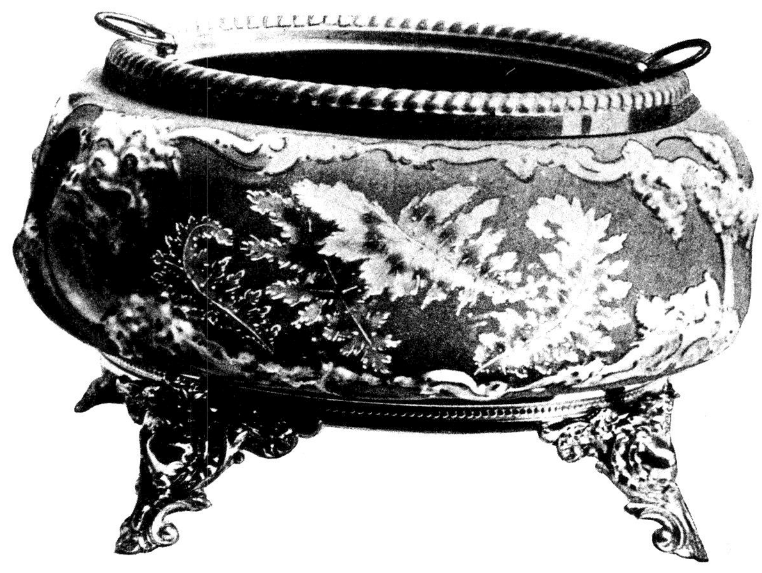

Fernery 388—S V.

Assortment 6, list each, . . $8.00

Fernery 205—I V.

Assortment 6, list each, . . $8.00

WAVE CREST WARE.

Patented October 4, 1892.

BUD VASES.

Gold plated trimmings and decorated bodies.

Cuts about one-half actual size.

Bud Vase Globe—F P.
Assortment 4, list each, . $1.30

Bud Vase 163—G P.
Assortment 4, list each, . $1.30

Bud Vase 175—P I.
Assortment 4, list each, . $1.50

Bud Vase 165—G P.
Assortment 4, list each, . $1.30

Bud Vase 177—F P.
Assortment 4, list each, . $1.30

Bud Vase 166—G P.
Assortment 4, list each, . $1.50

Bud Vase 184—G P.
Assortment 4, list each, $1.50

Bud Vase 310—Z R.
Assortment 4, list each, . $1.30

Vase 353—E P.
Assortment 4, list each, . $1.50

WAVE CREST WARE.

Patented October 4, 1892.

OPAL BUD VASES.

Gold plated trimmings and decorated bodies.

Cuts about one-half actual size.

Vase 282—G Y.

Assortment 4, list per dozen, $16.00

Bud Vase 156—H P.

Assortment 4, list each, $1.50

Bud Vase 174—I P.

Assortment 4, list each, $1.75

Bud Vase 281—O P.

Assortment 4, list each, $2.00

Vase Ornament 261—Q W.

Assortment 4, list per dozen, $18.00

Vase 416—B I.

Assortment 4, list each, $2.50

WAVE CREST WARE.

Patented October 4, 1892.

OPAL VASES.

Gold plated trimmings and decorated bodies.

Cuts about one-half actual size.

Vase 417—N I.

Assortment 4, list per dozen, . $16.00

Vase 283—H Y.

Assortment 4, list each, . $3.50

Vase 418—I T.

Assortment 4, list each, . $2 75

Vase 419—D I.

Assortment 4, list each, . . $2.50

Vase 414—Z N.

Assortment 4, list each, . $2.50

Vase 415—A I.

Assortment 4, list each, . $3.00

WAVE CREST WARE.

Patented October 4, 1892.

VASES.

Gold plated trimmings and decorated bodies.

Cuts about one-half actual size.

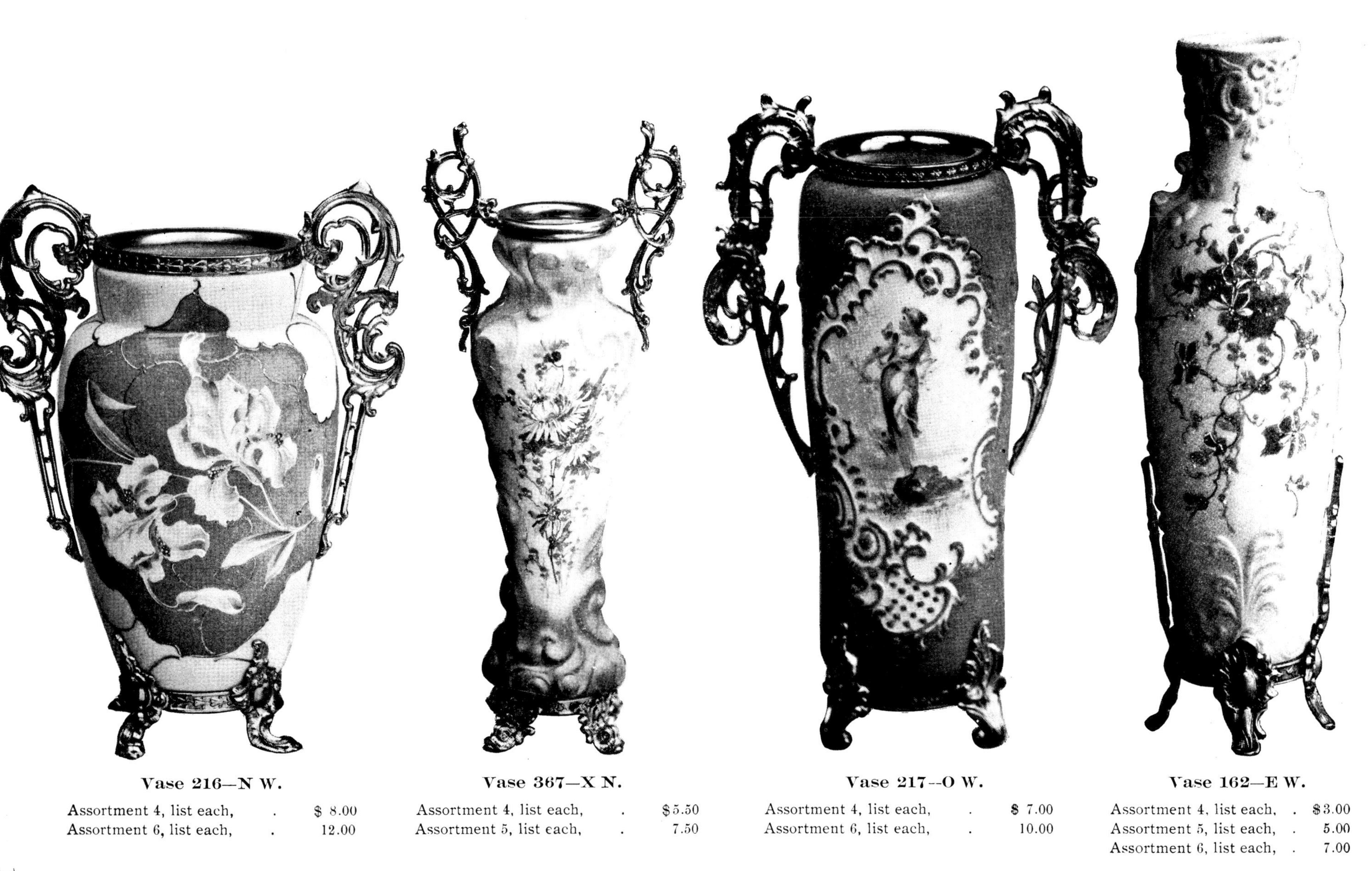

Vase 216—N W.

Assortment 4, list each, .	$ 8.00
Assortment 6, list each, .	12.00

Vase 367—X N.

Assortment 4, list each, .	$5.50
Assortment 5, list each, .	7.50

Vase 217—O W.

Assortment 4, list each, .	$ 7.00
Assortment 6, list each, .	10.00

Vase 162—E W.

Assortment 4, list each, .	$3.00
Assortment 5, list each, .	5.00
Assortment 6, list each, .	7.00

WAVE CREST WARE.

Patented October 4, 1892.

VASES.

Gold plated trimmings and decorated bodies.

Cuts about one-half actual size.

Vase 365—L P.

Assortment 4, list each,	.	$ 9.00
Assortment 5, list each,	.	11.00
Assortment 6, list each,	.	14.00

Vase 366—N P.

Assortment 4, list each,	.	$ 9.50
Assortment 5 list each,	.	13.50
Assortment 6, list each,	.	16.00

Vase 359—M P.

Assortment 4, list each,	.	$ 9.00
Assortment 5, list each,	.	13.00
Assortment 6, list each,	.	15.50

Vase 358—K P.

Assortment 4, list each,	.	$ 9.50
Assortment 5, list each,	.	13.50
Assortment 6, list each,	.	16.00

WAVE CREST WARE.

Patented October 4, 1892.

VASES.

Gold plated trimmings and decorated bodies

Cuts about one-half actual size.

Vase 384—L I.

Assortment 6, list each, . . $16.00

Vase 368—M I.

Assortment 6, list each, . $15.00

Vase 278—R Y.

Assortment 4, list each, . . $14.00

Assortment 6, list each, . . 24.00

WAVE CREST WARE.

Patented October 4, 1892.

LOVING CUPS.

Suitable for prizes.

Cuts about one-half actual size.

Loving Cup, No. 375—H I.

With silver mounting.

Assortment 6, list each, . . . $14.00

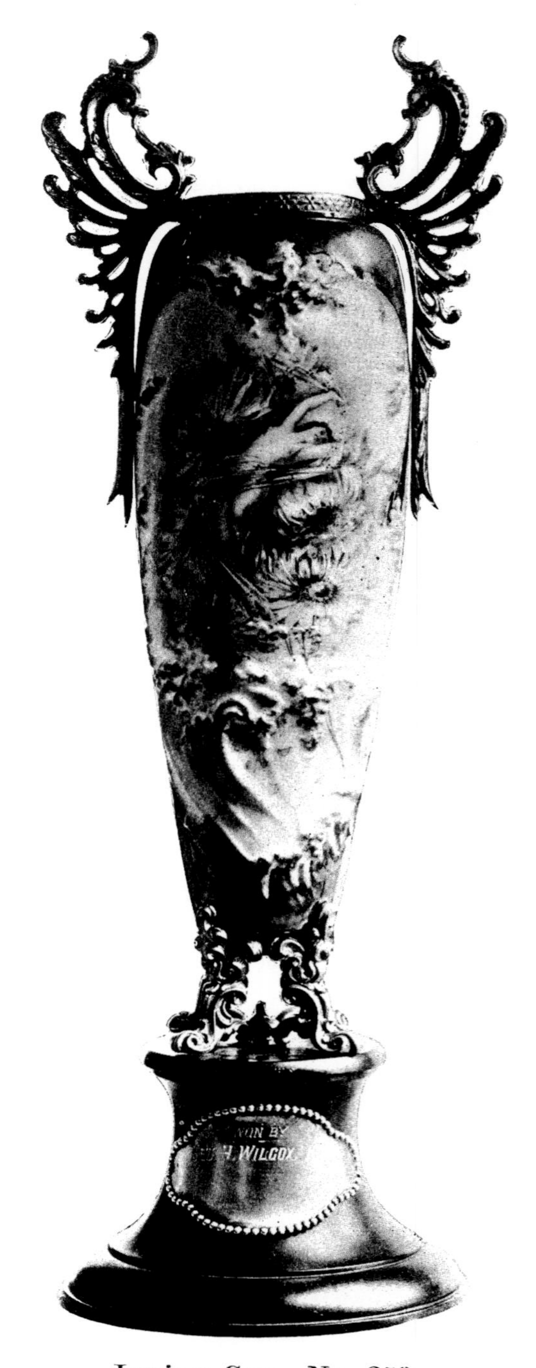

Loving Cup, No. 359.

With gold plated trimmings.

Assortment 6, list each, . . $30.00

Ebony base, sterling plate.

WAVE CREST WARE.

Patented October 4, 1892.

CANDELABRA.

Handsomely mounted with gold plated trimmings.

Cuts about one-half actual size.

Candelabrum 358—P L.

Assortment 5, list each, ... $32.00

Candelabrum 158—O L.

Assortment 6, list each, ... $22.00

WAVE CREST WARE.

Patented October 4, 1892.

CANDELABRA.

Handsomely mounted with gold plated trimmings.

Cuts about one-half actual size.

Candlestick 307—M S.

Assortment 4, list each,	.	$2.50
Assortment 6, list each,	.	3.00

Candelabrum 366—R L.

Assortment 5, list each,	.	$30.00

Candlestick 308—M S.

Assortment 4, list each,	.	$2.50
Assortment 6, list each,	.	3.00

WAVE CREST WARE.

Patented October 4, 1892.

PHOTO AND CARD RECEIVERS.

Mounted with gold plated trimmings.

Cuts about one-half actual size.

Card Receiver 312—W N.

Assortment 4, list each, . . . $3.50

Photo Receiver 167—K X.

Assortment 4, list each, . $2.00

Traced in Gold. Assortment 5, list each, . 4.00

Card Tray 181—R X.

Assortment 4, list each, . . . $1.25

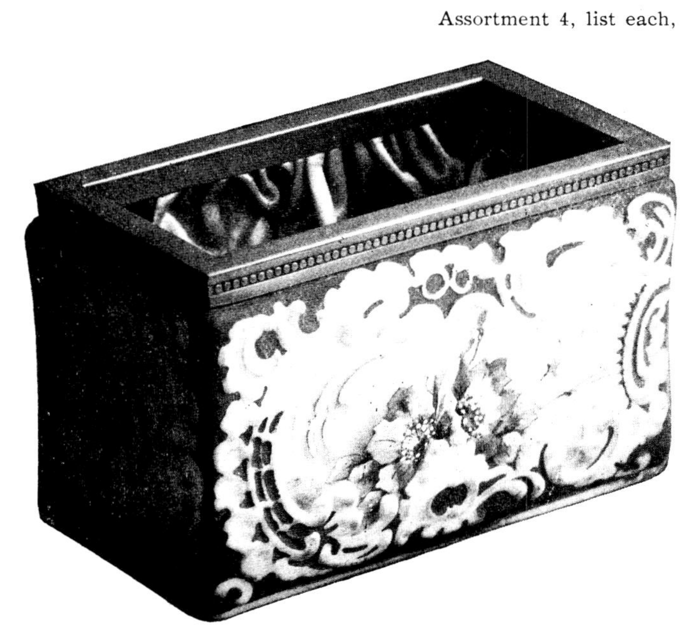

Photo Receiver 226—X V.

Takes a large photo 5¼ x 7½ inches. Embossed or Cameo surface.

Assortment 4, lined, list each, . . $3.00

Assortment 4, not lined, list each, . . 2.50

Photo Receiver 226—Z V.

Embossed or Cameo surface.

Assortment 4, lined, list each, . . . $4.50

Assortment 4, not lined, list each, . . . 4.00

WAVE CREST WARE.

Patented October 4, 1892.

JEWEL TRAYS.

Mounted with gold plated trimmings.

Cuts about one-half actual size.

Jewel Tray 424—A V.

Assortment 4, list per dozen, $9.00

Jewel Tray 237—B N.

Assortment 4, list each, . $2.00

Jewel Tray 398—B V.

Assortment 4, list per dozen, . $12.00

Jewel Tray 408—R S.

Assortment 4, list per dozen, . $22.00

Jewel Tray 373—A V.

Assortment 4, list per dozen, . $15.00

Jewel Tray 346—D P.

Assortment 4, list each, . . $2.50

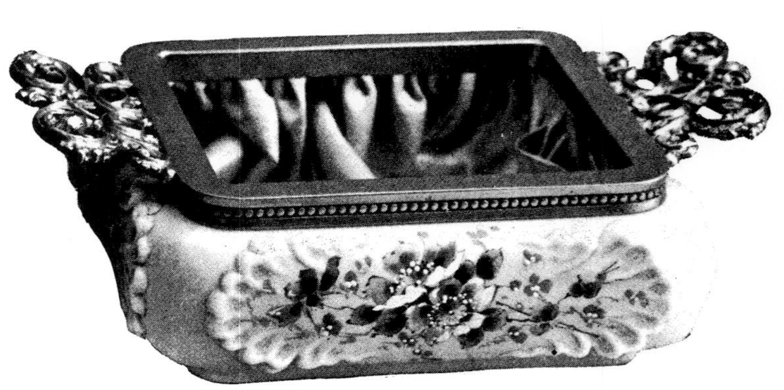

Jewel Tray 288—P Z.

Assortment 6, list each, . . $5.00

WAVE CREST WARE.

Patented October 4, 1892.

JEWEL TRAYS.

Mounted with gold plated trimmings.

Cuts about one-half actual size.

Jewel Tray 334—Y S.

Assortment 6, list each, . . $5.00

Jewel Tray 294—A N.

Assortment 4, list each, . . $3.50

Jewel Tray 142—R W.

Assortment 4, list each, . $3.00

Jewel Tray 264—R P.

Assortment 4, list each, . $6.50 Assortment 6, list each, . $10.00

WAVE CREST WARE.

Patented October 4, 1892.

JEWEL TRAYS.

Mounted with Gold plated trimmings.

Cuts about one-half actual size.

Cupid Jewel Tray 294—T P.

Assortment 4, list each, ...	$4.50
Assortment 6, list each, ...	6.50

Cupid Jewel Tray 274—V P.

Assortment 4 list each, . . .	$3.50
Assortment 6, list each, . . .	5.50

Cupid Jewel Tray 290—S P.

Assortment 4, list each, . . . $5.50

Cupid Jewel Tray 142—X P.

Assortment 4, list each, ...	$5.00
Assortment 5, list each, . . .	6.50

WAVE CREST WARE.

Patented October 4, 1892.

JEWEL TRAYS AND JEWEL STANDS.

Mounted with gold plated trimmings.

Cuts about one-half actual size.

Jewel Tray 280—H T.

Assortment 4, list each, . . $2.00

Jewel Stand 323—P N.

Assortment 4, list each, . . $2.25

Jewel Tray 294—V Z.

Assortment 6, list each, . . $5.00

Jewel Stand 218—R S.

Assortment 4, list each, . $2.50

Jewel Tray 256—D R.

Assortment 6, list each, . . $6.00

Jewel Stand 207—B V.

Assortment 4, list per dozen, . . $21.50

WAVE CREST WARE.

Patented October 4, 1892.

MIRROR TRAYS.

Mounted with gold plated trimmings.

Cuts about one-half actual size.

Mirror Tray 306—K S.

Assortment 4, list each, . . $5.00

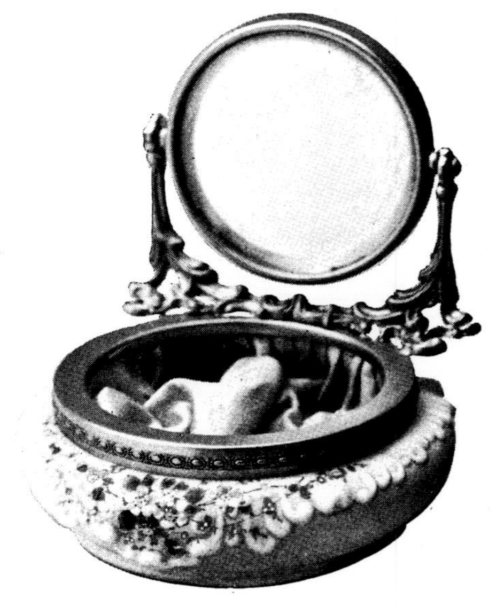

Mirror Tray 323—P S.

Assortment 4, list each, . $2.50

Mirror Tray 294—A S.

Assortment 4, list each, . . $4.00

Mirror Tray 294—B S.

Assortment 6, list each, . . $6.00

WAVE CREST WARE.

Patented October 4, 1892.

MIRROR TRAYS.

Mounted with gold plated trimmings.

Cuts about one-half actual size.

Mirror Tray 225—E Z.

Assortment 4, list each, . . . $7 00
Assortment 6, list each, . . . 8.00

Mirror Tray 306—L S.

Assortment 6, list each, . . . $8.00

WAVE CREST WARE.

Patented October 4, 1892.

COMB AND BRUSH HOLDER AND MIRROR TRAY.

Mounted with gold plated trimmings.

Cuts about one-half actual size.

Trinket, Comb and Brush Holder 238—P Y.

Assortment 4, list each, ... $5.00

Mirror Tray 264—F Z.

Assortment 6, list each, . . . $8.00

WAVE CREST WARE.

Patented October 4, 1892.

RING TRAYS, PINCUSHION AND COMB AND BRUSH TRAY.

Mounted with gold plated trimmings.

Cuts about one-half actual size.

Ring Tray 363—O N.

Assortment 4, list per dozen, . $24.00

Pincushion and Tray 377—L N.

Assortment 4, list per dozen, . . $20.00

Ring Tray 363—K N.

Assortment 4, list per dozen, . $15.00

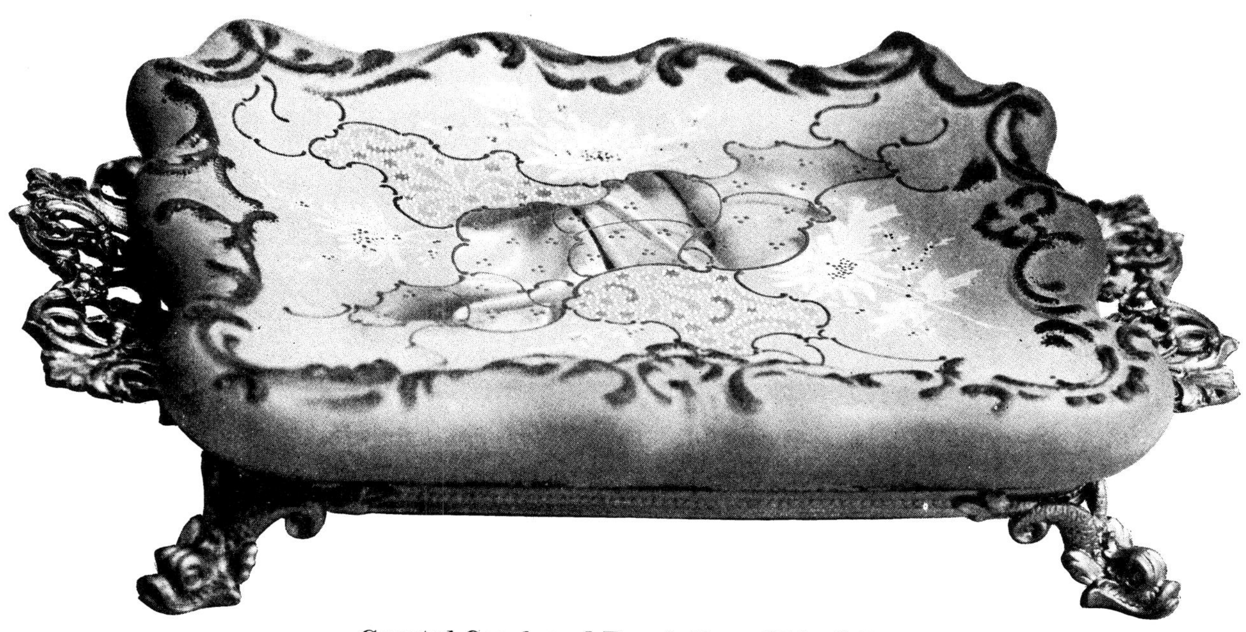

Crystal Comb and Brush Tray 354—C L.

Assortment 6, list each, ... $12.00

The body of this tray and decoration is most pleasing. The effect of the satin showing through the crystal is very novel and striking, and the whole makes a beautiful article and something entirely new.

WAVE CREST WARE.

Patented October 4, 1892.

HAIR RECEIVERS AND PUFF TRAYS.

Mounted with Gold Plated Trimmings.

Cuts about one-half actual size.

Hair Receiver 323—H S.

Assortment 4, list each, . . $1.50

Hair Receiver 231—S L.

Assortment 4, list per dozen, . . $12.50

Hair Receiver 294—W Z.

Assortment 4, list each, . . $1.70

Hair Receiver 305—H S.

Assortment 6, list each, . . $2.75

Puff Tray 320—A V.

Assortment 4, list per dozen, . . $10.00
Without Puffs, list per dozen, . . 8.50

Puff Tray 237—A V.

Assortment 4, list per dozen, . . $17.00
Without Puffs, list per dozen, . . 13 00

WAVE CREST WARE.

Patented October 4, 1892.

PUFF STANDS AND MIRROR PUFFS.

Mounted with gold plated trimmings.

Cuts about one-half actual size.

Puff Stand 206—W V.

Assortment 4, list per dozen, .	$19.00
Without Puffs, list per dozen, .	17.00

Puff Stand 218—A V.

Assortment 4, list per dozen, .	$27.00
Without Puffs, list per dozen, .	23.00

Mirror Puff 323—P S.

Assortment 4, list each, .	$2.50
Without Puffs, list each, . .	2.25

Mirror Puff 294—A S.

Assortment 4, list each, ...	$4.00
Without Puffs, list each, ...	3.75

Mirror Puff 294—B S.

Assortment 6, list each, ...	$6.00
Without Puffs, list each, ...	5.75

WAVE CREST WARE.

Patented October 4, 1892.

PUFF BOXES.

Mounted with gold plated trimmings.

Cuts about one-half actual size.

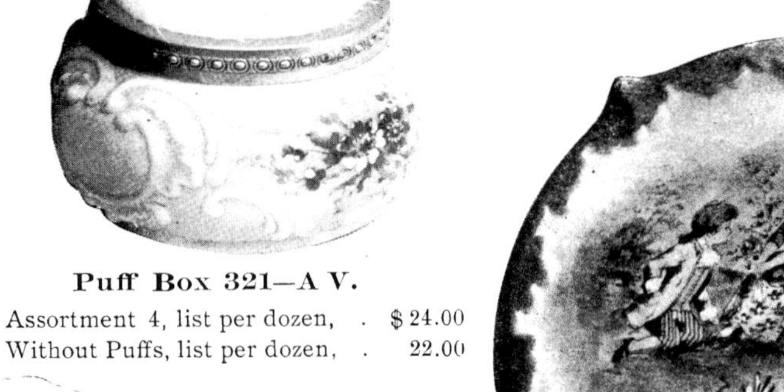

Puff Box 322—B Y.

Assortment 4, list per dozen, .	$28.00
Without Puffs, list per dozen, .	24.00

Puff Box 325—B Y.

Assortment 4, list per dozen, .	$24.00
Without Puffs, list per dozen, .	22.00

Puff Box 321—A V.

Assortment 4, list per dozen, .	$24.00
Without Puffs, list per dozen, .	22.00

Puff Box 293—T V.

Assortment 4, list each, ...	$4.00
Assortment 6, list each, ...	6.00
Without Puffs, Assortment 4, list each, . .	3.50
Without Puffs, Assortment 6, list each, . .	5.50

Puff Box 305—B Y.

Assortment 4, list per dozen, . .	$36.00
Without Puffs, list per dozen, . . .	32.00

Puff Box 392—N V.

Assortment 4, list each, . .	$5.50

WAVE CREST WARE.

Patented October 4, 1892.

POMADES, ATOMIZERS, SOAP DISHES, TOOTH POWDER AND TOOTH BRUSH HOLDERS.

Mounted with Gold Plated Trimmings.

Cuts about one-half actual size.

Pomade Box 262—E Y.

Assortment 4, list per doz., $10.00

178 Nickel Top, Plain Bulbs.

Assortment 1,	list per dozen,	$9.50
Assortment 2,	list per dozen,	10.00
Assortment 2½,	list per dozen,	10.00

156 Nickel Top, Plain Bulbs.

Assortment 2½,	list per dozen,	$16.00
Assortment 4,	list per dozen,	24.00
Assortment 5,	list per dozen,	32.00

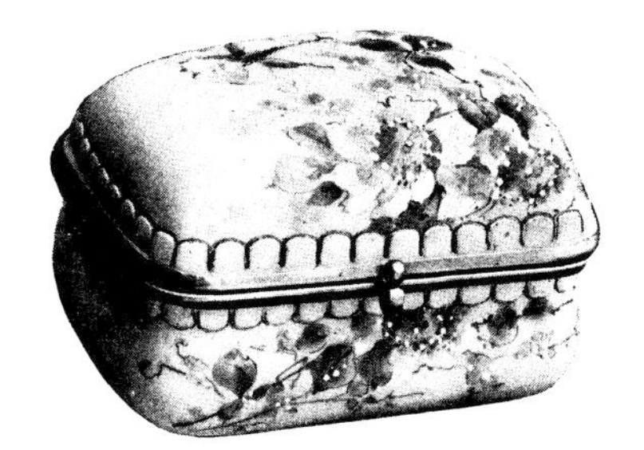

Soap Box 112.

Assortment 4, list per dozen, $9.00

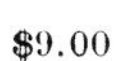

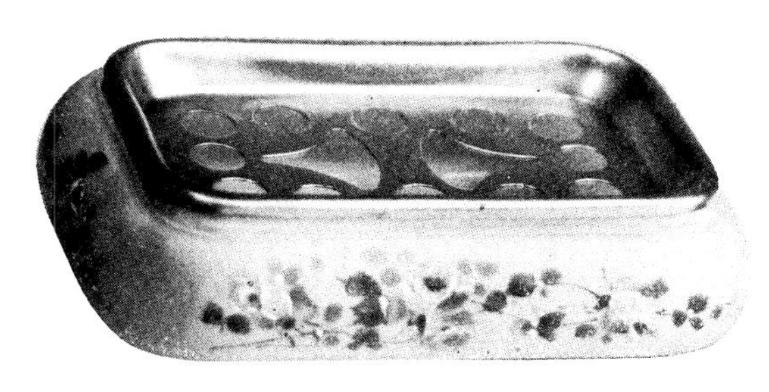

Soap Dish 379—D L.

Assortment 4, list per dozen, . $15.00
(Nickel Receptacle.)

Pomade Box 243—D Y.

Assortment 4, list per dozen, $6.00

Tooth Powder Box 244—D Y.

Assortment 4, list per dozen, $9.00

Tooth Brush Holder 245—D Y.

Assortment 4, list per dozen, $14.50

WAVE CREST WARE.

Patented October 4, 1892.

OPAL ATOMIZERS, DECORATED.

Mounted with Nickel or Gold Plated Trimmings, Netted or Plain Rubber Bulbs.

These are far superior to the cheap imported, being on a more artistic order.

For Netted Bulbs a charge is made of $1.00 more per dozen net, than for Plain Bulbs.
For Gold Plate a charge is made of $1.50 more per dozen net, than for Nickel Plate.

Cuts about one-half actual size.

Assortment 5, Traced in Gold.

173 Nickel Top, Netted Bulbs.
Assortment 4, list per dozen, $24.00

176 Nickel, Netted Bulbs.
Assortment 5, list per dozen, $32.00

166 Nickel Top, Netted Bulbs.
Assortment 4, list per dozen, $32.00
Assortment 5, list per dozen, 36.00

175 Gold, Netted Bulbs.
Assortment 5, list per dozen, $36.00

184 Gold, Netted Bulbs.
Assortment 5, list per dozen, $48.00
Assortment 6, list per dozen, 72.00

165 Gold, Netted Bulbs.
Assortment 5, list per dozen, $48.00
Assortment 6, list per dozen, 60.00

WAVE CREST WARE.

Patented October 4, 1892.

JEWEL BOXES.

Mounted with Gold Plated Trimmings.

Cuts about one-half actual size.

Jewel Box 423—A V.

Landscape Decorations.
Assort. 4, all lined, list per doz., $19.00
Assort. 4, not lined, for Bon-Bon, list per doz., ... 17.00

Jewel Box 324—A V.

Assort. 4, all lined, list per doz., $20.00
Assort. 4, not lined, for Bon-Bon, list per doz., ... 17.00

Jewel Box 321—A V.

Assort. 4, Floral Decorations, list each, $2.00
Assort. 4, Cupid Decorations, list each, 2.30

Jewel Box 325—A V.

Assort. 4, all lined, list per doz., $24.00
Assort. 4, not lined, for Bon-Bon, list per doz., ... 22.00

Jewel Box 395—A V.

Assortment 4, list per dozen, $22.00

Jewel Box 322—A V.

Assort. 4, Floral Decorations, list each, $2 50
Assort. 4, Cupid Decorations, list each, 2.70

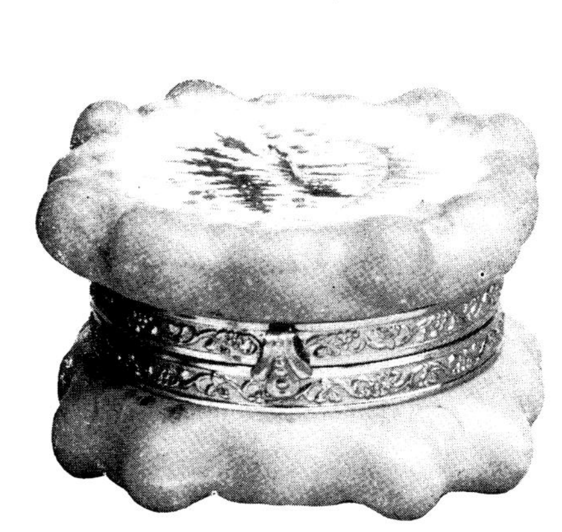

Jewel Box 373—B Y.

Assortment 4, list each, $2.50

Jewel Box 407—B Y.

Landscape Decorations.
Assort. 4, all lined, list per doz., $30.00
Assort 4, not lined, for Bon-Bon, list per doz., ... 24.00

Jewel Box 305—A V.

Assort. 4, all lined, list per doz., $36.00
Assort. 4, not lined, for Bon-Bon, list per doz., ... 32.00

WAVE CREST WARE.

Patented October 4, 1892.

JEWEL BOXES.

Mounted with Gold Plated Trimmings.

Cuts about one-half actual size.

Jewel Box 425—W V.

Assortment 4, list each, $3.00

Oval Jewel Box 405—W V.

Assortment 4, all lined, list per dozen, . $30.00

Jewel Box 397—A V.

Cupid Decorations.

Assort. 4, all lined, list per doz., $24.00

Assort. 4, not lined, for Bon-Bon, list per doz., . . . 22.00

Jewel Box 319—O S.

Assortment 4, list each, . $2 50

Jewel Box 409—B Y.

CRYSTAL.—The effect of the satin showing through the crystal is very pleasing.

Assortment 4, list each, . $2.50

Jewel Box 304—Y N.

Assortment 4, list each, . $3.00

Jewel Box 425—A Z.

Assortment 4, Cupid Decorations, list each, $4.00

WAVE CREST WARE.

Patented October 4, 1892.

CLOCK JEWEL AND JEWEL BOXES.

Mounted with Gold Plated Trimmings.

Cuts about one-half actual size.

Jewel Box 191—T S.

Assortment 4 list each, . $3.00
Traced in Gold. Assortment 5, list each, . 4.50

Jewel Box 293—A V.

Assortment 4, list each, . $4.50

Jewel Box 326—B Y.

Assortment 4, list each, . $3.00
Assortment 6, list each, . 5.00

Clock Jewel 346—A V.

Assortment 4, list each, . $7.00

Jewel Box 403—B Y.

Cupid Decorations only.
Assortment 4, list each, . $3.50

Jewel Box 273—B Y.

Assortment 4, Floral Decorations, list each, $4.00
Assortment 4, Cupid Decorations, list each, 4.50

WAVE CREST WARE.

Patented October 4, 1892.

JEWEL BOXES.

Mounted with Gold Plated Trimmings.

Cuts about one-half actual size.

Crystal Jewel Box 345—G I.

Assortment 5, list each, . $5.00

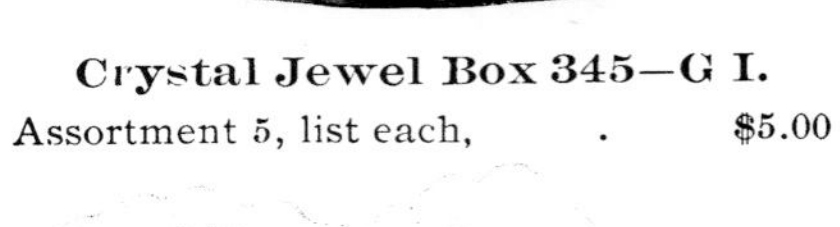

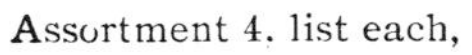

Jewel 392—G I.

Assortment 4. list each, . $4.00

Jewel 168—S O.

Assortment 4, list each, . $3 50

Jewel Box 327—T S.

Assortment 4, list each, . $5.00

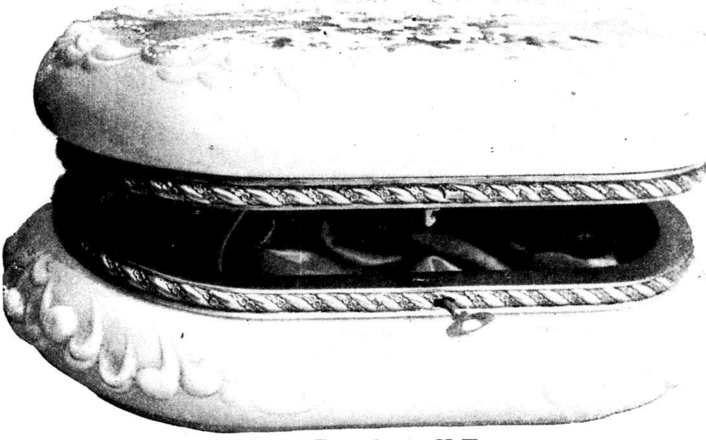

Jewel Box 255—X T.

Assortment 4, list each, . $5.50

Jewel Box 288—T T.

Assortment 4, Cupid Decorations only, list each, . $7.00

WAVE CREST WARE.

Patented October 4, 1892.

JEWEL BOXES.

Mounted with gold plated trimmings.

Cuts about one-half actual size.

Jewel Box 273—C Y.

Gold Traced. Assortment 5, list each, . $5.50

Jewel Box 234—E V.

Assortment 4, list each, . $7.00
Assortment 6, list each, . 9 00

Jewel Box 327—W S.

Assortment 6, list each, . $11.00

Jewel Box 331—Z O.

Assortment 6, list each, . $10.00

WAVE CREST WARE.

Patented October 4, 1892.

JEWEL AND HANDKERCHIEF BOXES.

Mounted with Gold Plated Trimmings.

Cuts about one-half actual size.

Jewel Box 255—O Y.

Assortment 6, list each, . $7.50

Jewel Box 293—T Z.

Assortment 5, list each, . $7.00

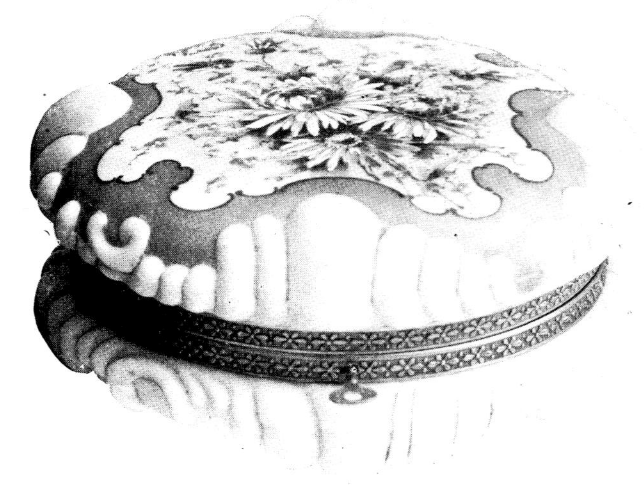

Handkerchief Box 190—T S.

Assortment 4, list each, . $4.50

Traced in Gold. Assortment 5, list each, . 6.00

Handkerchief Box 303—W V.

Assortment 4, list each, . . $4 50

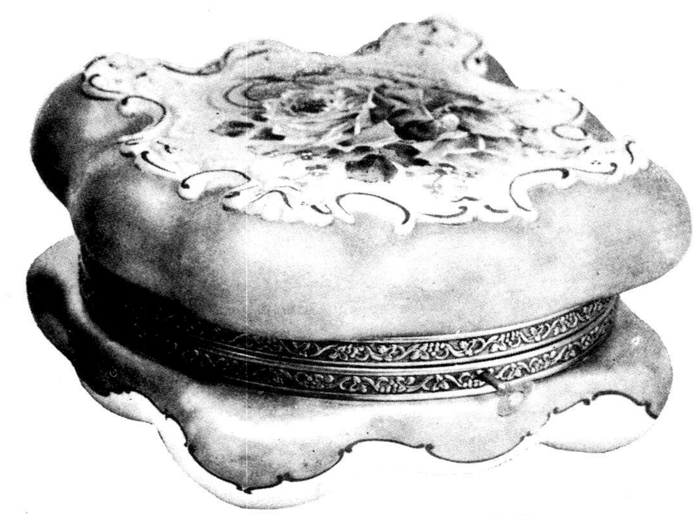

Handkerchief Box 328—B Y.

Assortment 4, list each, ... $5.00

Assortment 6, list each, . . . 7.00

Handkerchief Box 429—B Y.

Cupid Decorations only.

Assortment 4, list each, . . $5.00

WAVE CREST WARE.

Patented October 4, 1892.

OPAL HANDKERCHIEF BOXES.

Mounted with Gold Plated Trimmings.

Cuts about one-half actual size.

Opal Handkerchief Box 428—G I.

Assortment 6, list each, ... $10.00

Opal Handkerchief Box 354—D Z.

Assortment 5, list each, ... $14.00
Assortment 6, list each, ... 20.00

WAVE CREST WARE.

Patented October 4, 1892.

CRYSTAL HANDKERCHIEF BOXES.

Mounted with Gold Plated Trimmings.

Cuts about one-half actual size.

Crystal Handkerchief Box 372—B Y.

Assortment 6, Crystal, list each, ... $12.00
Assortment 5, Opal, list each, ... 9.00

Crystal Handkerchief Box 385—G I.

Assortment 5, list each, ... $6.00

Crystal Handkerchief Box 354—D Z.

Assortment 6, list each, ... , . . $17.00

This style of decoration is entirely new, and the effect of the satin showing through the crystal is most pleasing, and makes a rich, beautiful and novel article.

WAVE CREST WARE.

Patented October 4, 1892.

OPAL HANDKERCHIEF BOXES.

Mounted with Gold Plated Trimmings

Cuts about one-half actual size.

Handkerchief Box 430—G I.

Assortment 4, list each, ... $6.00

Handkerchief Box 260—A V.

Assortment 4, list each, ... $5.00

Handkerchief Box 296—R V.

Assortment 4, list each, ... $5.00

WAVE CREST WARE.

Patented October 4, 1892.

HANDKERCHIEF BOXES.

Mounted with Gold Plated Trimmings.

Cuts about one-half actual size.

Handkerchief Box 390—B Y.

Assortment 4, list each, ... $5.50

Handkerchief Box 297—D S.

Assortment 6, list each, ... $8.50

Handkerchief Box 387—E S.

Assortment 6, list each, ... $14.00

WAVE CREST WARE.

Patented October 4, 1892.

HANDKERCHIEF BOXES.

Mounted with Gold Plated Trimmings.

Cuts about one-half actual size.

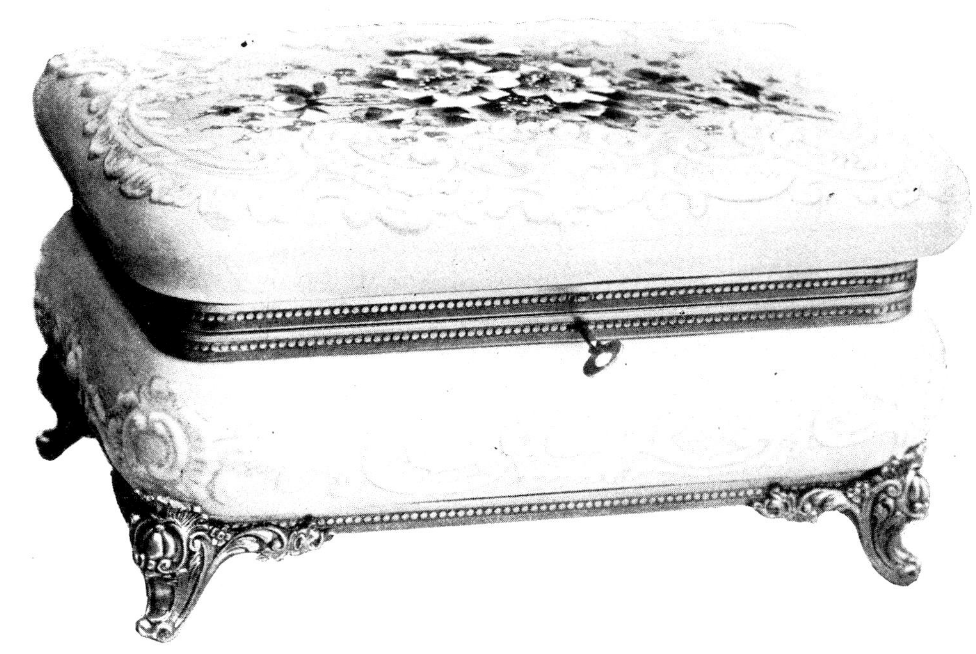

Handkerchief Box 224—E V.

Assortment 4, list each, ...	$10.00
Assortment 6, list each, ...	12.00

Handkerchief Box 263—K Y.

Traced in Gold.	Assortment 5, list each, . . .	$14.00
	Assortment 6, list each, . . .	18.00

WAVE CREST WARE.

Patented October 4, 1892.

HANDKERCHIEF BOX AND MANICURE TRAY.

Mounted with Gold Plated Trimmings.

Cuts about one-half actual size.

Handkerchief Box 329--W S.

Assortment 6, list each, . . . $15.00

Combination Manicure Tray and Jewel Boxes 401—C L.

Assortment 4, list each, . $10.00

Traced in Gold. Assortment 5, list each, . $12.00

WAVE CREST WARE.

Patented October 4, 1892.

OPAL AND CRYSTAL GLOVE BOXES.

Mounted with Gold Plated Trimmings.

Cuts about one-half actual size.

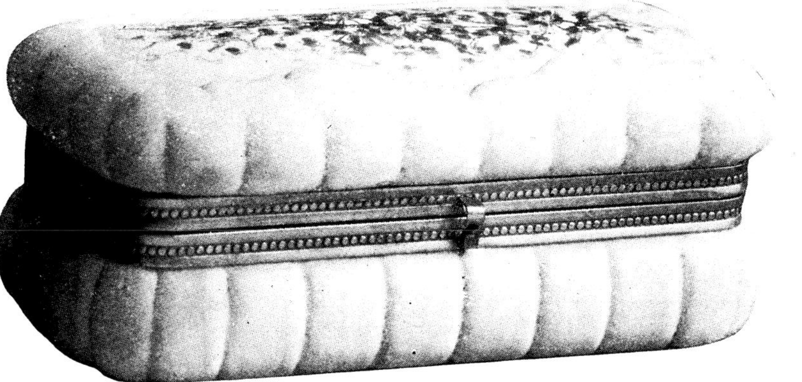

Glove Box 253—N Y.
Assortment 4, list each, ... $6.00

Crystal Glove Box 349—T T.
Assortment 5, list each, ... $10.00

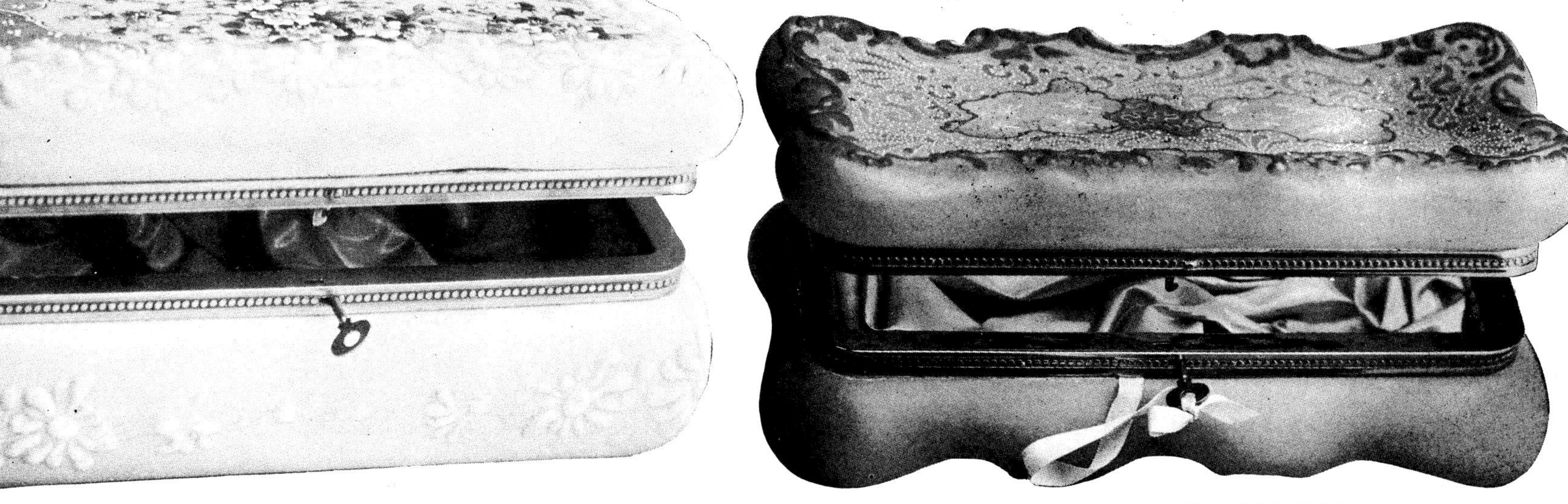

Glove Box 291—T T.
Assortment 5, list each, ... $8.00
Assortment 6, list each, ... 12.00

Crystal Glove Box 356—T T.
Assortment 6, list each, ... $11.00

WAVE CREST WARE.

Patented October 4, 1892.

OPAL GLOVE BOXES AND MANICURE BOX.

Glove Box 291—E V.
Assortment 6, list each, ... $13.50

Figure Decoration on Cover to 291—E V. .

Glove Box 232—E V.
Assortment 4, list each, ... $9.00
Assortment 6, list each, ... 13.50

Manicure Set 303—A V.
Assortment 4, list each, ... $12.00
Complete with Sterling Silver Manicure Set, 6 pieces.

WAVE CREST WARE.

Patented October 4, 1892.

MANICURE BOXES.

Handsomely Mounted with Gold Plated Trimmings.

Cuts about one-half actual size.

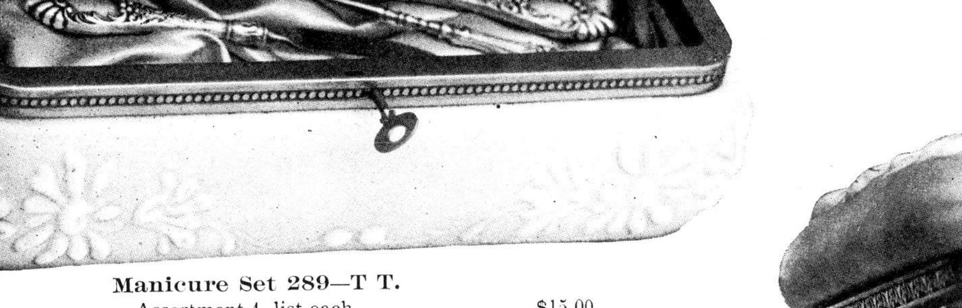

Manicure Set 289—T T.

	Assortment 4, list each, ...	$15.00
Traced in Gold.	Assortment 5, list each, ...	16.00
	Assortment 6, list each.	20.00

Complete, with Sterling Silver Manicure Set, 6 pieces.

Manicure Set 333—M Y.

Assortment 4, list each, ...	$11.00
Assortment 6, list each, ...	15 00

Complete, with Sterling Silver Manicure Set, 4 pieces.

Manicure Set 263—K Y.

Traced in Gold.	Assortment 5, list each, ...	$23.50
	Assortment 6, list each, ...	27.50

Complete, with Sterling Silver Manicure Set, 6 pieces.

WAVE CREST WARE.

Patented October 4, 1892.

WHISKEY FLASK, WHISK BROOM AND HOLDERS.

Mounted with Gold Plated Trimmings.

Cuts about one-half actual size.

Whiskey Flask 364—F L.

Assortment 4, list each, ...	$3.00
Assortment 5, list each, ...	4.00
Assortment 6, list each, ...	5.50

Sterling Top.

Whisk Broom Holder 228—Z S.

Assortment 4, list each, ... $4.00

Whisk Broom Holder 223—K W.

Assortment 4, list each, ... $3.50

Whisk Broom 63—E L.

Assortment 1, list per dozen, .	$6.70
Assortment 2½, list per dozen, .	7.00

WAVE CREST WARE.

Patented October 4, 1892.

INK STANDS WITH REMOVABLE INK WELLS.

Mounted with Gold Plated Trimmings.

Cuts about one-half actual size.

Ink Stand 314—M R.

Assortment 4, list each, . . $3.00
Assortment 6, list each, . . 4.00

Pen Wiper 262—E P.

Assortment 4, list per dozen, $13.50

Ink Stand 399—S N.

Assortment 4, list each, . $2.50

Ink Stand 361—S N.

Assortment 4, list each, . . . $2.50

Ink Stand 315—R N.

Assortment 4, list each, . . . $3.00

Ink Stand 315—N R.

Assortment 4, list each, ... $4.50
Assortment 6, list each, ... 7.50

Ink Stand 361—T N.

Assortment 4, list each, ... $3.00
Assortment 6, list each, ... 6.00

WAVE CREST WARE.

Patented October 4, 1892.

PAPER WEIGHTS, FILES AND BLOTTERS.

With Gold Plated Trimmings.

Cuts about one-half actual size.

Paper Weight 201—G W.

Assortment 4, list per dozen, . $8.50

Paper Weight 201—H W.

Assortment 4, list per dozen, . $9.00

Paper Weight 202—F W.

Assortment 4, list per dozen, $14.00

Gold Traced. Assortment 5, list per dozen, 20.00

Blotter 277—X S.

Assortment 4, list each, . $2.00

Blotter 332—T W.

Assortment 4, list each, . $1.50

Assortment 6, list each, . 3.00

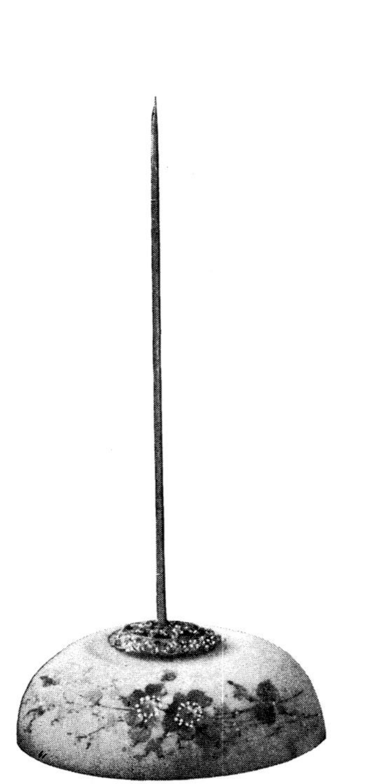

Memo-File 202—B W.

Assortment 4, list per dozen, $8.50

Memo-File 201—C W.

Assortment 4, list per dozen, $9.00

Assortment 5, list per dozen, 15.00

Memo-File 202—D W.

Assortment 4, list per dozen, $13.00

Gold Traced. Assortment 5, list per dozen, 18.00

WAVE CREST WARE.

Patented October 4, 1892.

POKER CHIP BOXES AND CARD CASE.

Mounted with Gold Plated Trimmings.

Cuts about one-half actual size.

Card Case 250½—I Y.

Assortment 4, list each, . .	$1.20
Assortment 6, list each, . .	2.50
Cards, Gilt Edged, per pack, list each,	.50

Poker Chip Box 289—M Z.

Including 264 Poker Chips and one Pack of Cards, Gilt Edged.

	Assortment 4, list each, complete, . . .	$10.00
Gold Traced.	Assortment 5, list each, complete, . . .	15.50

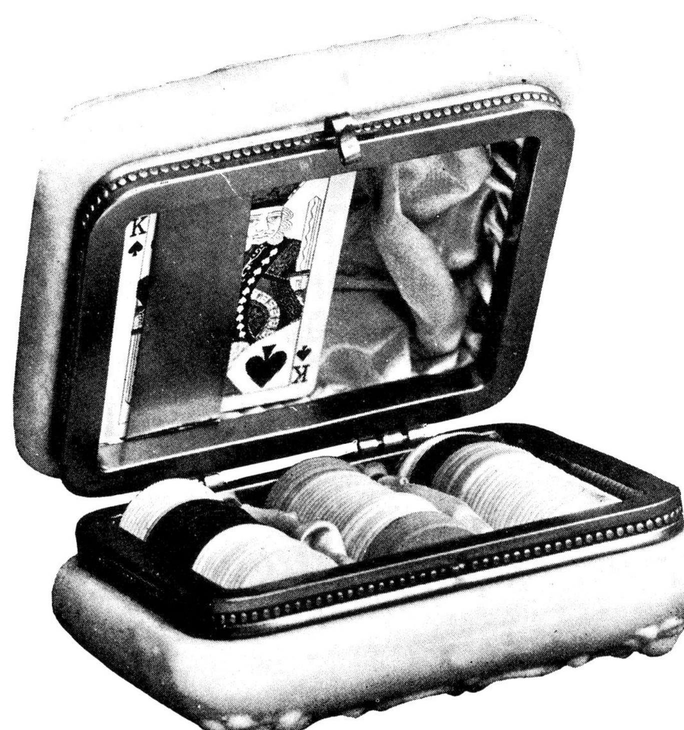

Poker Chip Box 287—M Z.

Including 108 Poker Chips and one Pack of Cards, Gilt Edged.

Assortment 4, list each, complete, ... $6.50

WAVE CREST WARE.

Patented October 4, 1892.

Mounted with Gold Plated Trimmings.

Cuts about one-half actual size.

Cigar Set 215—Y O.

Assortment 4. list each, . . $3.00

Gold Traced. Assortment 5, list each, . . 5.00

Cigar Holder 215—I O.

Assortment 4, list per dozen, . $18.00

Cigar Box 224—Z Y.

Assortment 4, list each, ... $7.00

Receptacle for moistener in top of cover.

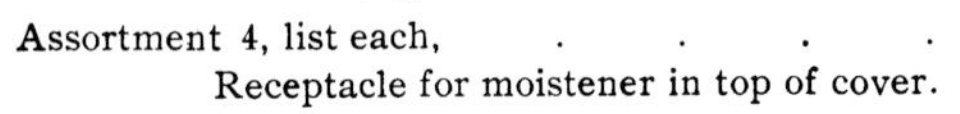

Cigar Box 329—O X.

Assortment 4, list each, ... $6.50

Receptacle for moistener in top of cover.

WAVE CREST WARE.

Patented October 4, 1892.

CIGAR AND TOBACCO JARS.

Mounted with Gold Plated Trimmings. Having Receptacle in Top of Cover for Moistener.

Cuts about one-half actual size.

Cigarette Jar 337—Y Y.

Assortment 4, list each,	. . . .	$2.00
Assortment 6, list each,	. . . .	4.00

Cigar Jar 335—H R.

Assortment 4, list each,	. . . . .	$4.50
Assortment 6, list each,	. . . . .	7.00

Cigar Jar 336—H R.

Assortment 4, list each,	. . . .	$4.50
Assortment 6, list each,	. . . . .	7.00

With Spring Lock and Key.

Tobacco Jar 170—X Y.

Assortment 4, list each,	. . . .	$2.50

WAVE CREST WARE.

Patented October 4, 1892.

MATCH HOLDERS.

Mounted with Gold Plated Trimmings.

Cuts about one-half actual size.

Match Holder 214—H O.

Assortment 4, list per dozen, . $8.50
Assortment 5, list per dozen, . 10.00

Match Holder 309—N S.

Assortment 4, list per dozen, . $9.00

Match Holder 262—H O.

Assortment 4, list per dozen, . $9.50

Combination Ash Tray and Match Holder 321—B L.

Assortment 4, list each, . $2.00

Combination Ash Tray and Match Holder 346—N L.

Assortment 4, list each, . $3.00

Safety Match Holder 378—K L.

Assortment 4, list each, $1.70

Match Safe 265—V T.

Assortment 4, list per dozen, . $15.00

Safety Match Holder 378—M L.

Assortment 4, list each, $2.30

WAVE CREST WARE.

Patented October 4, 1892.

ASH TRAYS AND RECEIVERS.

Mounted with Gold Plated Trimmings.

Cuts about one-half actual size.

Ash Tray 320—A V.
Assortment 4, list per dozen, . $8.50

Ash Tray 320—V O.
Assortment 4, list per dozen, . $9.50

Ash Tray 424—D V.
Assortment 4, list per dozen, . $9.50

Ash Tray 171—G N.
Assortment 4, list each, . . $2.00

Ash Receiver 202—W O.
Assortment 4, list each, . . $1.20

Ash Tray 294—F N.
Assortment 4, list each, . . $2.25

Ash Receiver 218—U W.
Assortment 4, list per dozen, . $27.00

Ash Tray 396—V O.
Assortment 4, list per dozen, . $16.50

Golf Ash Tray 242—H N.
Assortment 4, list each, . $1.50

Ash Tray 410—W W.
Assortment 4, list each, . $1.50

WAVE CREST WARE.

Patented October 4, 1892.

COLLAR AND CUFF BOXES.

Mounted with Gold Plated Trimmings.

Cuts about one-half actual size.

Collar and Cuff 212—A V.

Assortment 4, list each, ... $5.00

Collar and Cuff 329—Y T.

Assortment 4, list each, ... $6 50

Collar and Cuff 260—Y T.

Assortment 4, list each, ... $6.00

Collar and Cuff 298—L R.

Assortment 4, list each, ... $7.00

WAVE CREST WARE.

Patented October 4, 1892.

Cuts about one-half actual size.

Call Bell 218—Y W.

Assortment 4, list each, ... $3.50

Bon-Bon with Bail 142—G Z.

Silver Plated. Assortment 4, list each, . . $3.50
Silver Plated. Assortment 5, list each, . . 4.50
Extra charge for Gold Plate, list each, ...50

Bon-Bon with Bail 141—H Z.

Silver Plated. Assortment 4, list each, . $2.50
Silver Plated. Assortment 5, list each, . 3.50
Extra charge for Gold Plate, list each, . . .50

Fern Bell 260—Z W.

Assortment 4, list each, ... $5.00

A Novelty, designed for Dining Table, having a rotary Gong Bell that cannot be seen, it being under the Fern Dish. A most useful and ornamental Table Piece.

WAVE CREST WARE.

Patented October 4. 1892.

SUGAR AND CREAM SETS.

With Silver Plated Trimmings.

Cuts about one-half actual size.

SUGAR AND CREAM SET.

Sugar 138—Y. **Cream 139—Y.**

	Assortment 4, list per set, ...	$4.00
Traced in Gold.	Assortment 5, list per set, ...	5.50

Sugar 316—B T. **Cream 317—B T.**

Assortment 4, list per set, ... $5.00

Sugar 122—B X. **Cream 123—B X.**

	Assortment 4, list per set, ...	$6.00
Traced in Gold.	Assortment 5, list per set, ...	7.00

WAVE CREST WARE.

Patented October 4, 1892.

SYRUPS AND SUGAR SIFTERS.

Cuts about one-half actual size.

Syrup 53—U X.

Assortment 1, list each,	.	$1.25
Assortment 4, list each,	.	1.50
Assortment 5, list each,	.	2.50

Syrup 317—N Z.

Assortment 4, list each, $2.50

Sugar Sifter 53—A A.

Assortment 1,	list per dozen,	$2.50
Assortment 2,	list per dozen,	3.00
Assortment 2½,	list per dozen,.	3.00

Sugar Sifter 53—D D.

Assortment 1,	list per dozen,	$6.00
Assortment 2,	list per dozen,	7.00
Assortment 4,	list per dozen,	9.00
Gold Traced. Assortment 5,	list per dozen,	15.00

Syrup 100—S.

Assortment 1,	list per dozen,	$3.00
Assortment 2,	list per dozen,	3.50
Assortment 2½,	list per dozen,	3.50

WAVE CREST WARE.

Patented October 4, 1892.

CRACKER JARS.

With Silver Plated Trimmings.

Cuts about one-half actual size.

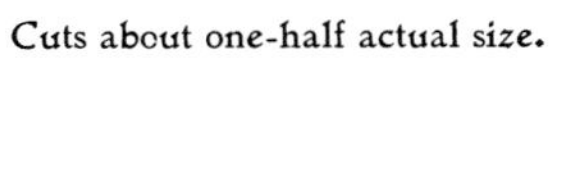

12—G X.

Assortment 2, list each, . . $1.80
Assortment 2½, list each, . 2.00

285—G X.

Assortment 2½, list each, . . $2.50

404—G X.

Assortment 2½, list each, . . $2.50

404—V K.

Assortment 2½, list each, . . $2.50

WAVE CREST WARE.

Patented October 4, 1892.

CRACKER JARS.

Silver Plated Trimmings.

Cuts about one-half actual size.

285—D T.
Assortment 4, list each, . $4.50
Gold Traced. Assortment 5, list each, . 7.00
D T Trimmings, Gold Plated, list each, 50c extra.

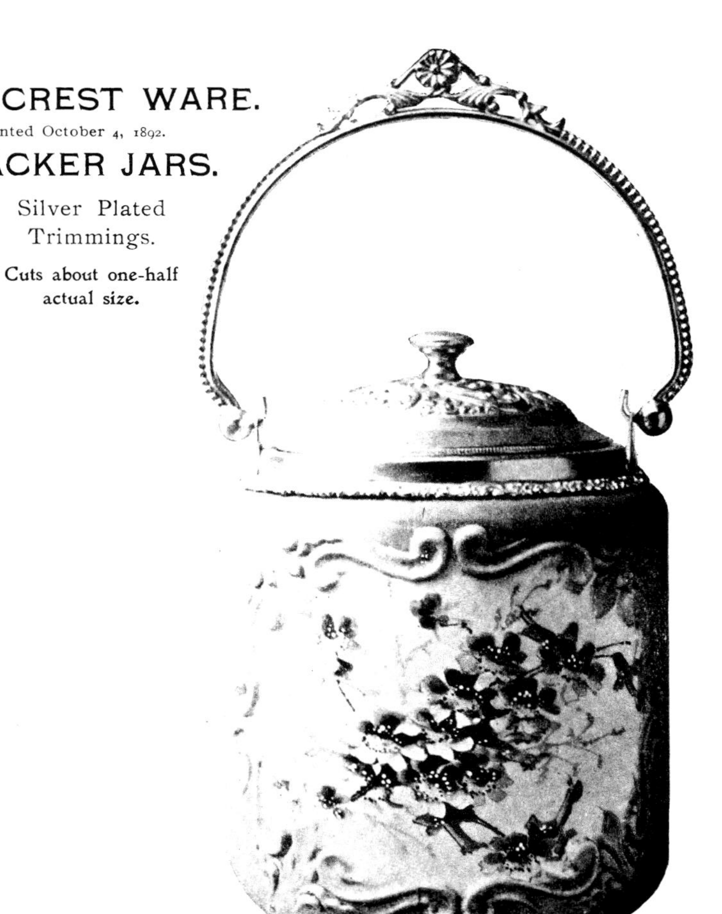

404—D T.
Assortment 4, list each, . $4.50

402—T K.
Assortment 4, list each, . . $3.50

402—V K.
Assortment 2½, list each, . . $2.50

WAVE CREST WARE.

Patented October 4, 1892.

CRACKER JARS.

With Silver Plated Trimmings.

Cuts about one-half actual size.

393—T K.

Assortment 4, list each, $3.00

260—I Z.

Assortment 4, list each, $5.50

Gold Traced. Assortment 5, list each, . 8.50

271—W K.

Assortment 4, list each, . . $3.50

352—V K.

Assortment 2½, list each, . . $2.50

OPAL SALTS AND PEPPERS, DECORATED, IN 6 DIFFERENT ASSORTMENTS.

The following cuts of Salts are about one-third actual size.

DESCRIPTION OF ASSORTMENTS.

Asst. 1 consists of 6 Decorations on White Ground, Glazed.
Asst. 2 consists of 6 Decorations on Tinted Ground, Glazed.
Asst. 2½ consists of 6 Decorations on Tinted Ground, Bisque Finish, same Design as Asst. 2.
Asst. 3 consists of 6 Dec. on Tinted Ground, Glazed, designs more elaborate.
Asst. 4 consists of 6 Dec. on Tinted Ground, Bisque Finish, same Design as Asst. 3.
Asst. 5 consists of 6 Dec. on Tinted Ground, Bisque Finish, Design more elaborate with Gold.

67—A A.
Asst. 1, per gro. list, $14 00
Asst. 2, per gro. list, 15 00
Asst. 2½, per gro. list, 18 00

67—B B.
Asst. 1, per gro. list, $18 00
Asst. 2, per gro. list, 19 00
Asst. 2½, per gro. list, 24 00
Asst. 4, per gro. list, 30 00
Asst. 5, per gro. list, 42 00

67—C C.
Asst. 1, per gro. list, $24 00
Asst. 2, per gro. list, 25 00
Asst. 2½, per gro. list, 27 00
Asst. 4, per gro. list, 33 00
Asst. 5, per gro. list, 45 00

68—A A.
Asst. 1, per gro. list, $14 00
Asst. 2, per gro. list, 15 00
Asst. 2½, per gro. list, 18 00

68—B B.
Asst. 1, per gro. list, $18 00
Asst. 2, per gro. list, 19 00
Asst. 2½, per gro. list, 24 00
Asst. 4, per gro. list, 30 00
Asst. 5, per gro. list, 42 00

68—C C.
Asst. 1, per gro. list, $24 00
Asst. 2, per gro. list, 25 00
Asst. 2½, per gro. list, 27 00
Asst. 4, per gro. list, 33 00
Asst. 5, per gro. list, 45 00

69—A A.
Asst. 1, per gro. list, $14 00
Asst. 2, per gro. list, 15 00
Asst. 2½, per gro. list, 18 00

69—C C.
Asst. 1, per gro. list, $24 00
Asst. 2, per gro. list, 25 00
Asst. 2½, per gro. list, 27 00
Asst. 3, per gro. list, 30 00
Asst. 4, per gro. list, 33 00

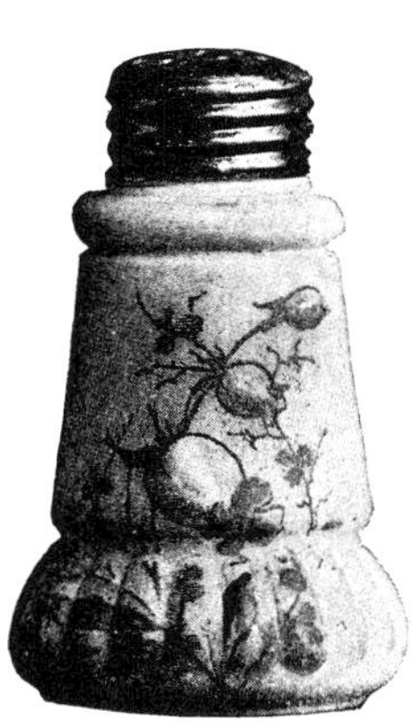

70—A A.
Asst. 1, per gro. list, $14 00
Asst. 2, per gro. list, 15 00
Asst. 2½, per gro. list, 18 00

70—B B.
Asst. 1, per gro. list, $18 00
Asst. 2, per gro. list, 19 00
Asst. 2½, per gro. list, 24 00

70—C C.
Asst. 1, per gro. list, $24 00
Asst. 2, per gro. list, 25 00
Asst. 2½, per gro. list, 27 00

72—A A.
Asst. 1, per gro. list, $14 00
Asst. 2, per gro. list, 15 00
Asst. 2½, per gro. list, 18 00

72—B B.
Asst. 1, per gro. list, $18 00
Asst. 2, per gro. list, 19 00
Asst. 2½, per gro. list, 24 00
Asst. 3, per gro. list, 27 00
Asst. 4, per gro. list, 30 00

73—A A.
Asst. 1, per gro. list, $14 00
Asst. 2, per gro. list, 15 00
Asst. 2½, per gro. list, 18 00

73—B B.
Asst. 1, per gro. list, $18 00
Asst. 2, per gro. list, 19 00
Asst. 2½, per gro. list, 24 00
Asst. 3, per gro. list, 27 00
Asst. 4, per gro. list, 30 00
Asst. 5, per gro. list, 42 00

OPAL SALTS AND PEPPERS.

Decorated in 6 Assortments. 6 Decorations in each Assortment.

The first number designates the shape of article, the letters the style of cap, and the next number the assortment of decorations.

A A is a Nickel Plate Cap, Single Screw. B B Silver Plate Cap, Single Screw. C C Silver Plate Cap, Double Screw.

73—C C.

Asst. 1,	per gro. list,	$24 00
Asst. 2,	per gro. list,	25 00
Asst. 2½,	per gro. list,	27 00
Asst. 3,	per gro. list,	30 00
Asst. 4,	per gro. list,	33 00
Asst. 5,	per gro. list,	45 00

96—A A.

Asst. 1,	per gro. list,	$14 00
Asst. 2,	per gro. list,	15 00
Asst. 2½,	per gro. list,	18 00

96—B B.

Asst. 1,	per gro. list,	$18 00
Asst. 2,	per gro. list,	19 00
Asst. 2½,	per gro. list,	24 00

96—C C.

Asst. 1,	per gro. list,	$24 00
Asst. 2,	per gro. list,	25 00
Asst. 2½,	per gro. list,	27 00

97—A A.

Asst. 1,	per gro. list,	$14 00
Asst. 2,	per gro. list,	15 00
Asst. 2½,	per gro. list,	18 00

97—B B.

Asst. 1,	per gro. list,	$18 00
Asst. 2,	per gro. list,	19 00
Asst. 2½,	per gro. list,	24 00
Asst. 4,	per gro. list,	30 00

98—A A.

Asst 1,	per gro. list,	$14 00
Asst 2,	per gro. list,	15 00
Asst. 2½,	per gro. list,	18 00

98—B B.

Asst. 1,	per gro. list,	$18 00
Asst. 2,	per gro. list,	19 00
Asst. 2½,	per gro. list,	24 00
Asst. 4,	per gro. list,	30 00
Asst 5,	per gro. list,	42 00

98—C C.

Asst. 1,	per gro. list,	$24 00
Asst. 2,	per gro. list,	25 00
Asst. 2½,	per gro. list,	27 00
Asst. 4,	per gro list,	33 00
Asst. 5,	per gro. list,	45 00

79—D D.

Asst. 1	per gro. list,	$28 00
Asst. 2,	per gro. list,	30 00
Asst. 2½,	per gro. list,	33 00
Asst. 3,	per gro. list,	36 00
Asst. 4,	per gro. list,	39 00
Asst. 5,	per gro. list,	48 00

H H NICKEL TOP. MUSTARDS. I I SILVER PLATE TOP.

80—D D.

Asst. 1,	per gro. list,	$20 00
Asst. 2,	per gro. list,	30 00
Asst. 2½,	per gro. list,	33 00
Asst. 3,	per gro. list,	36 00
Asst. 4,	per gro. list,	39 00
Asst. 5,	per gro. list,	48 00

79—H H.

Asst. 1,	per gro. list,	$19 00
Asst. 2,	per gro. list,	20 00
Asst. 2½,	per gro. list,	23 00

79—I I.

Asst. 1,	per gro. list,	$30 00
Asst. 2,	per gro. list,	32 00
Asst. 2½,	per gro. list,	36 00
Asst. 3,	per gro. list,	39 00
Asst. 4,	per gro. list,	42 00
Asst. 5,	per gro. list,	54 00

80—H H.

Asst. 1,	per gro. list,	$19 00
Asst. 2,	per gro. list,	20 00
Asst. 2½,	per gro. list,	23 00

80—I I.

Asst. 1,	per gro. list,	$30 00
Asst. 2,	per gro. list,	32 00
Asst. 2½,	per gro. list,	36 00
Asst. 3,	per gro. list,	39 00
Asst. 4,	per gro. list,	42 00
Asst. 5,	per gro. list,	54 00

WAVE CREST WARE.

Patented October 4, 1892.

SALTS, PEPPERS AND TOOTHPICK HOLDERS.

Cuts about one-third actual size.

A A is Nickel Plate Cap, Single Screw.
B B is Silver Plate Cap, Single Screw.
C C is Silver Plate Cap, Double Screw.
E E is Silver Plate Cap, Double Screw.

338—A A.
Asst. 1, list per gro. $14 00
Asst. 2, list per gro. 16 00
Asst. 2½, list per gro. 19 00

338—B B.
Asst. 2½, list per doz. $2 50
Asst. 4, list per doz. 3 00

204—B B.
Asst. 2½, list per doz. $2 50
Asst. 4, list per doz. 3 00

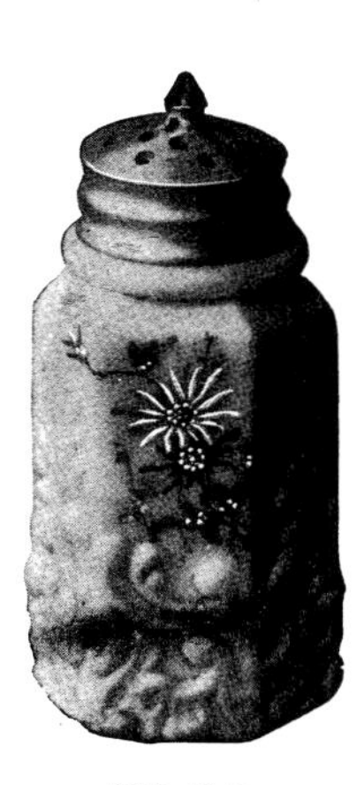

203—B B.
Asst. 2½, list per doz. $2 50
Asst. 4, list per doz. 3 00

383—B B.
Asst. 2½, list per doz. $2 50
Asst. 4, list per doz. 3 00

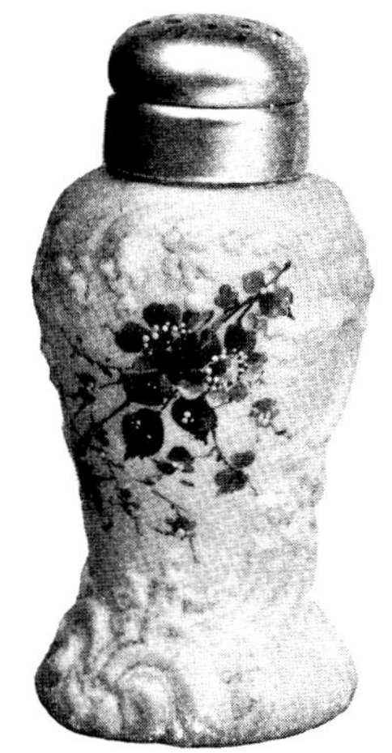

383—C C.
Asst. 4, list per dozen, $4 00
Asst. 5, list per dozen, 6 00
Asst. 6, list per dozen, 8 00

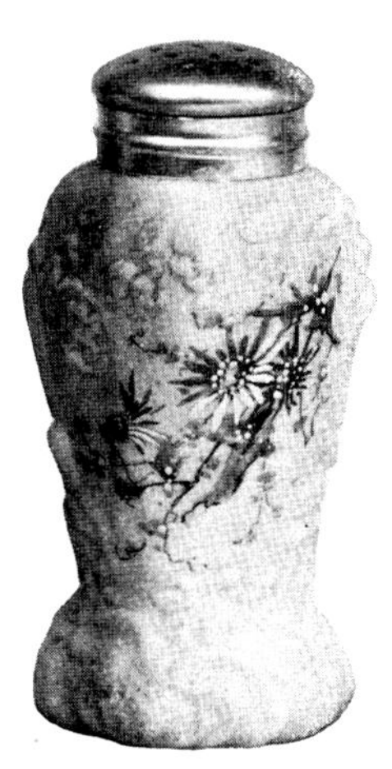

383—E E.
Asst. 4, list per dozen, $4 00
Asst. 5, list per dozen, 6 00
Asst. 6, list per dozen, 8 00

382—A A.
Asst. 1, list per gro. $14 00
Asst. 2, list per gro. 16 00
Asst. 2½, list per gro. 19 00

382—B B.
Asst. 2½, list per doz. $2 50
Asst. 4, list per doz. 3 00

382—E E.
Asst. 4, list per dozen, $4 00
Asst. 5, list per dozen, 6 00
Asst. 6, list per dozen, 8 00

351—G G.
Assortment 4, list per dozen, $3.00

129—E E.
Assortment 4, list per dozen, $4 00
Assortment 5, list per dozen, 6 00
Assortment 6, list per dozen, 8 00

339—E E.
Assortment 4, list per dozen. $4 00
Assortment 5, list per dozen, 6 00
Assortment 6, list per dozen, 8 00

65. Open Salt.
Assortment 1, list per gross, $14 00
Assortment 4, list per gross, 24 00

99. Tooth Pick.
Assortment 1, list per gro. $12 00
Assortment 2, list per gro. 14 00
Assortment 2½, list per gro. 14 00
Assortment 4, list per gro. 30 00
Assortment 5, list per gro. 39 00

THE PARKER NON-CORROSIVE SALT.

Patented July 4, 1899.

Which the C. F. Monroe Company have secured the sole rights to Manufacture and Decorate.

Cuts about three-fourths actual size.

Showing opening of Salt, filled from top, before adjusting non-corrosive cap.

Showing top of Salt A, with perforated Crystal Glass and Metal Trimming, before adjusting.

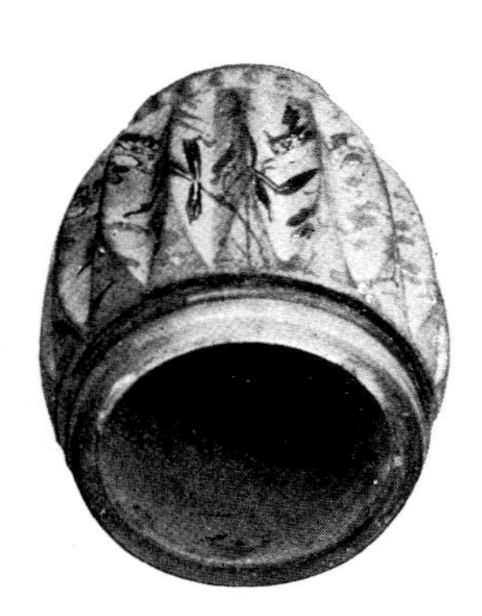

Showing opening of Salt, filled from bottom, made with perforated Glass Top.

Showing the bottom of Salt C with Crystal Glass and Metal Trimming.

Salts "A" and "C" are made in Opal with a perforated crystal glass top held on with a metal band, which, when screwed on, presses the top glass to that of the bottle, thereby preventing salt from coming in contact with the metal, making it absolutely non-corrosive. Another great advantage of the crystal top is that you can always tell whether Salt is filled without taking off top. This article is destined to have an enormous sale.

Style A, with Silver Plated Band, extra, list per dozen, $2.00.
Style A fills from top, C from the bottom.

The Parker Salt.—A. Opal.

Opening from top.

Perforated Glass Top, Nickel Band.

Assortment 1,	list per dozen,	$4 00
Assortment 2,	list per dozen,	4.50
Assortment 2½,	list per dozen,	4.50
Assortment 4,	list per dozen,	5.50
Assortment 5,	list per dozen,	8.00

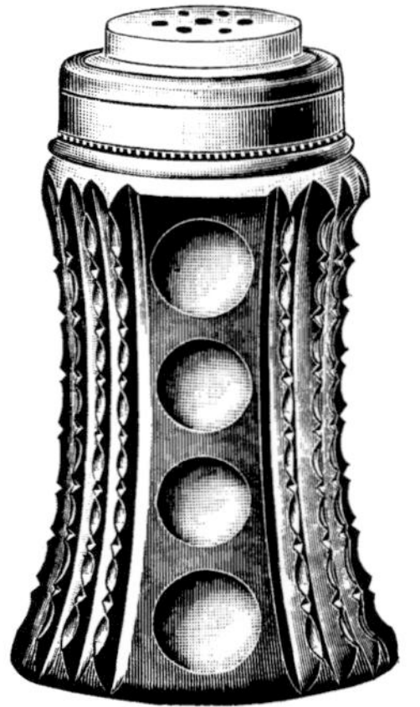

The Parker Salt 17.—Crystal.

No. 17, list per gross,	$27.00
No. 18, list per gross,	33.00
No. 19, list per gross,	33.00

No. 17 has nickel plated band, opening at top.

No. 18 has silver plated band, opening at bottom, same shape as Opal Salt "C."

No. 19 has silver plated band, opening at bottom, similar in shape to No. 17.

The Parker Salt.—C. Opal.

Opening from bottom.

Perforated Glass Top, Silver Plated Band.

Assortment 1,	list per dozen,	$7.00
Assortment 2,	list per dozen,	7.50
Assortment 2½,	list per dozen,	7.50
Assortment 4,	list per dozen,	8.50
Assortment 5,	list per dozen,	11 00

Decorated Opal Globe. 10-inch Decorated Opal Dome.

PRICE LIST OF GLOBES AND SHADES.

Princess Globes.

Height, about 4½ inches, 2¾ inch Holder. Prices per dozen, Net, from $3.00, $3.50, $4,00, $6.00, $9.00, $12.00. and upwards.

Argand Globes.

For Banquet and Stand Lamps. Height, 7 and 10 inches. 4-inch Holder. Prices per dozen, Net, from $9.00, $12.00, $15.00, $18.00, $21.00, $24.00, $36.00, and upwards.

10-inch Domes.

Assortment 3990.	Glazed, White Ground, Assorted Decorations, per dozen, list ,	$8.50
Assortment 3980.	Glazed, Tinted Ground, Assorted Decorations, per dozen, list,	9.00
Assortment 3960.	Bisque, Tinted Ground, Assorted Decorations, per dozen, list,	10.00
Assortment 600.	Bisque, Tinted Ground, Assorted Decorations, per dozen, list,	12.00
Assortment 610.	Bisque, Tinted Ground, Assorted Decorations, per dozen, list,	15.00
Assortment 620.	Bisque, Tinted Ground, Assorted Decorations, per dozen, list,	18.00
Assortment 630.	Bisque, Tinted Ground, Assorted Decorations, per dozen, list,	24.00
Assortment 640.	Bisque, Tinted Ground, Assorted Decorations, per dozen, list,	30.00
Assortment 650.	Bisque, Tinted Ground, Assorted Decorations, per dozen, list,	36.00
Assortment 660.	Bisque, Tinted Ground, Assorted Decorations, per dozen, list,	42.00
Assortment 670.	Bisque, Tinted Ground, Assorted Decorations, per dozen, list,	48.00
Assortment 680.	Bisque, Tinted Ground, Assorted Decorations, per dozen, list,	54.00
Assortment 690.	Bisque, Tinted Ground, Assorted Decorations, per dozen, list,	60.00

PRICES IN THIS CATALOGUE TO TAKE THE PLACE OF ALL PREVIOUS QUOTATIONS.

CORRESPONDENCE SOLICITED.